# THORSTEIN OF THE MERE

THURSTON WATER

W. G. COLLINGWOOD

# THORSTEIN OF THE MERE

## A SAGA

## OF THE NORTHMEN

## IN LAKELAND

*With an Introduction by*

EDWARD THOMPSON

*& a frontispiece drawn*

*by the Author*

LONDON

WILLIAM HEINEMANN LTD.

First published 1895 (Edward Arnold)
Reissued 1905 (Titus Wilson)
Cheap Reprint 1909 (Titus Wilson)
Reissued in new format 1929 (William Heinemann)
New Impression, April 1930

*Printed in Great Britain at*
THE WINDMILL PRESS, KINGSWOOD
*Surrey*

## DEDICATION

Thorstein is yours.    You've made him yours
By masterful appropriation ;
As long as right of might endures
I dare no other dedication,
Whatever name allures.

You've seized my copy and revise,
Absorbed the proofs, devoured the pages,
Retold the tale in travesties,
And sketched and played the personages
In many a quaint disguise.

Thanks, Robin : for the wide world o'er
A writer asks no finer flattery,
No kinder fate of all in store
Than Five-years-old's assault and battery
Demanding more and more.

But now to risk the wider test.
Of one applauding hand I'm certain ;
Let doubts and fears go unconfessed ;
So, stop the fiddle, lift the curtain
And, puppets, play your best.

# PREFACE

THESE verses were made for a little boy, now a man who knows much more than "Thorstein" taught him. He can afford to smile at this reminiscence of early days, long before he had dug forts and written "Roman Britain."

The story was meant as a picture of his home as it might have been, a thousand years ago. The outline was sketched from hints in place-names and from scraps of real history; the shading is frankly romantic. There are other books for the study of Lake district antiquities, and yet, as now printed, this ought not to be very grossly misleading to any reader who can discount its obvious extravagances.

And if there are uncouth words in it, and a rough, rustic style, it is because the tale was to be told in local dialect, familiar to a properly-brought-up child in these parts. Any child, with the opportunity, can be bilingual or even trilingual; but the easiest way to all knowledge is to begin at home.

# INTRODUCTION

*In* 1910, *William Canton (whom some will remember for " A Child's Book of Saints ") pointed to a photograph and said, " That's Collingwood. He writes as well as any man living." A few months later he sent me, about to sail for India, " Dutch Agnes Her Valentine," " to my mind worth a wilderness of novels." But " Dutch Agnes " is a novel, for its perfect background of Lakeland scenery and seasons is merely the illumination of a story hard to overpraise for lifelike quality. Canton urged me to let the author know of my gratitude ; I did so, thereby beginning what later ripened into friendship, although (except for one afternoon at Coniston, in* 1919) *friendship confined to correspondence.*

*Mr. Collingwood's versatility has been one thing that has kept him from recognition. Through many years he was Ruskin's secretary and unselfish friend, and many know him only for a " Life of Ruskin," which held the field previous to Sir E. T. Cook's fuller study, which Ruskin's death had made possible. " The Lake Counties," (*1902*) is such a guidebook as no other district can match, on every page marked by his fastidious care for accuracy and apparently inexhaustible knowledge of the history and antiquities of northern England. He was once Professor of Fine Art at what is now the University of Reading, and an accessible example of his own artistic achievement is his marvellously beautiful*

" *Northumbrian Crosses,*" *recently published by Messrs. Faber & Gwyer. He was W. P. Ker's predecessor in the presidency of the Viking Society, and of his* " *Pilgrimage to the Sagasteads of Iceland,*" *I have heard Mr. John Masefield break out in praise, asking* " *Why does not some publisher reissue it?* " *The answer is, in both England and America together there are not five hundred people sufficiently interested and able to afford to buy such a book. Blake used to assert of his prophetic books that, though without reputation on earth, they had a great angelic vogue. Even so, the* " *Sagasteads* " *and* " *Cormac the Skald,*" *though probably not a score of people in these islands know of them, in Iceland are recognised as the best books any foreigner has written about the country.*

*But my present purpose is to write a brief note on Mr. Collingwood's fiction.* " *I went out of the* ' *pure literature* ' *business long ago,*" *he once told me. His stories, re-creations of the past of that Lake District which he probably knows and loves better than any other man, have been one with his effort to understand for himself the sources from which the present flows.* " *That's what I like about Collingwood,*" *Canton (if I may quote him once more) once burst out;* " *there's a whole world of antiquarian knowledge behind every sentence.*" *There is all this, and a great deal more. But the author himself has been content that his books should be issued by local publishers, and on sale in Lake District stationers' shops.*

*Yet they have found a public; for the first edition of "Thorstein" you have to pay much more than its original price.*

*To conclude with a bibliographical note—which was all I was asked by the publishers to provide—"Thorstein" appeared on Lakeland stalls in 1895. Next year came "The Bondwoman." This, like Thorstein, found a London publisher and was quickly sold out. It was not reprinted, because it was thought by some "improper," the "Spectator," for example, remarking, "This is a book that ought never to have been written." This fact may serve as the measure of how low was the standard of impropriety thirty years ago and of how greatly we have since advanced; in this powerful, pitying study of elemental passions among a semi-civilised folk there is nothing to offend the most squeamish of circulating library readers to-day. "Coniston Tales," in 1899, contains nothing that is not characteristic and original; it includes at least one first-rate story, "The Cairn on the Moor," and some of his best verse. In 1910 came "Dutch Agnes Her Valentine," in my judgment his finest novel; and in 1917, "The Likeness of King Elfwald," whose mood and atmosphere are of the same mellow loveliness, but the story itself is interrupted by a long episode. Mr. Collingwood's other publications are very numerous, especially his contributions to the Cumberland and Westmorland Antiquarian and Archeological Society's "Transactions."*

Edward Thompson

# CONTENTS

# CONTENTS—*continued*

# CHAPTER 1

## THE COMING OF THE NORTHMEN

THERE was a man called Swein, who came into our country once upon a time, and built a house at Greenodd on the Leven. His father Biorn had been a landholder in Norway, ploughing his own acres, and living in health and wealth, until King Harald Fairhair fell upon the people, and fought with them and made himself lord and master. Then, it is well known, good men of the old sort, who could not abide to see new laws made and old laws undone, took to their ships and sailed away west. Some of them landed in Iceland; some went to Orkney, and others wandered about the coasts of the Irish Sea to find a home; and wherever they could get shelter and safety, there they settled.

Biorn, with his people and his young child Swein, came to the South Isles, as they called them then—the Western Isles we call them nowadays. He lived as best he might, and died at last in battle, when Harald swept the vikings from out of the seas between Lewis and Man. But Swein found

friends and plenty of work; for there was always
farming to do in spring and fighting in summer;
and in the end he wedded well, and sat down under
Bardi Ottarson, who was then the chief among the
Northmen in the Isle of Man. For by this time
Ketel Flatnose and his folk were gone to Iceland,
and the good King Orry was not yet come
therefrom.

Unna was wife to Swein Biornson. She was
the child of a viking akin to Olaf the White, the
great King of Dublin, and her mother was Irish.
Unna was a notable dame, and Swein was the sort
of man who could serve his friends; so that they
were both well thought of in the island, and hoped
for a safe home there. But before long came
Ragnwald the Dane, of the sons of Ivar, he that
was king in Waterford for a little while afterwards;
and he killed Bardi and most of his people in a sea-
fight.

Then Swein fled out of the battle hastily, and
took his wife and whatever he could lay hands on,
and steered for the far-away blue fells that showed
under the morning sun, over against the Manx
fells. For he knew that some of his kinsfolk had
already found lodging on the coasts of Galloway
and Cumberland and Wales, where the land was
no man's land at that time; and creeks and firths
among the hills gave them sheltered hiding places,
well out of sight when great fleets swept the high
seas and ravaged the open shore.

When Black Comb grew tall on the sky-line,
arose a stormy north-easter, and drove him down

the Cumberland coast, until he made Furness, the great foreland in the bay of Morecambe. When the wind fell, the tide flowed, and carried him up a broad firth like a gate into the hills. Upward he drifted, spying on all sides for a good landing spot ; and try as he might to the shoreward, he ran upon sand, and never came nigh the soil. But in a while he turned round a green point, high and rocky and covered with trees, standing out into the deep channel. Behind it was a green field, even with the water, snug and sheltered among hanging woods. A great beck flowed through the field to meet the broad firth. There were no people to be seen, nor smoke of houses, nor cattle about in the good lea-land. And the channel of the river at last came in-shore. So he stayed there, and called that green point in his language *Græn Oddi*, and Greenodd it is called to this day.

## CHAPTER II

### THE HOMESTEAD AT
### GREENODD

ONCE upon an afternoon in summer time it was
that our story begins. Swein and his people had
not been ten winters yet at Greenodd; but they
had built a good house, and cleared land to farm
it, and made the place look something like home.

So one afternoon before summer was over,
Unna sat rocking her baby Thorstein to sleep, and
sewing as she stirred the cradle with her foot, and
singing as she sewed. She wore a long gown of
ruddy colour, long sleeved; with a kerchief round
her neck, and a housewife's apron; but because
she was of high birth, she had a gold band like a
crown round her head, and her yellow hair was
tucked around it and fell away unbraided from
under a high white cap. A silken pocket hung
from her belt, and on her finger was a gold ring;
but her jewels for the most part were locked away
in a kist, against high-days and holidays. For this
was a working day, and everyone was busy.

Most folk were out of doors that time of year;
only the mother was at home, minding the baby
after her morning's turn round the farm; and to
keep her company, an old nurse who, being a

brisk body, was putting in a spell of work at a standing loom of the ancient make. She threw the shuttle slowly, and combed up the web but slackly, for the afternoon was warm, and the sun outside beat upon the roof of the house and made it hot. For the house was like one of our barns with its rafters and beams unceiled : and though it was heavily thatched, the air was hot within. It was somewhat gloomy too, in spite of the bright sheen that lay on field and fell. Though door and porch-door stood open, the rest of the place was lit only by windows that stood high up near the roof, in a row on either side of the long hall : and they were filled with bladder, which kept out the sun. One spot there was which had been burst by the stone-throwing of the boys, and not mended yet for want of hands in this busy summer-time. Through the hole a ray of sunlight shot across the hall, and caught on the chain of the hanging lamp, and lit up the thin smoke that rose in the midst. For the hearth fire was never let out if they could help. Even in summer it was needed morning and evening for their cooking and bad to kindle from fire-stones and rotten sticks. So as wood and peat were plentiful, it was smothered between whiles just to keep it alight, and thus went on from year's end to year's end.

The hearth was in the middle of the floor, then-a-days, raised a little and paved with cobbles set in clay. One could sit round it, as you can still at a fire-spot in a farm-house of the right old sort. And grand times they had of winter's evenings with their great chat fires, or else logs of which one end was out at the door while the other was blazing under the black pot. There folk would sit working and tale-telling, and watching acorns and crab apples roast, and the boiling of their porridge in that same great pot that hung by an iron crook and a chain from the house-beam over-head, the " rannal balk " as our folks, the Northmen's children, call it still.

Up through the gloom and the little space of sun went the thin blue smoke, like a stripe of rain out of April clouds. Half way to the roof it was met by the chimney flue, that hung down likest of ought to a great bell hanging from the roof tree, narrow at the top and covered like a belfry with a flagstone laid flat upon pillars, but opening out beneath and crossed by the house-beam. And in this luffer or chimney hung the last hams and smoked meat of the year before. For at the back end of the year they always hung their flesh meat against the winter, and Unna was too wise a house-wife to let them eat all up before the next store was laid in, however plentiful the season might be.

You must know this " firehouse " (as we still say) was the main hall and living room of the homestead. Bedchambers there were alongside of it behind the wall, and out-buildings ; not to say lofts among the beams, and an earth-house or cellar dug out under the floor at one end of

the hall. But the fire-house was the House as
one may say; and in a homely spot like this
backwood bigging at Greenodd a thousand years
since, everything went forward in the firehouse;
cooking and eating, work and play, business and
pleasure. This was their hearth and home.

At one corner were its door and porch opening
upon the garth, and at the opposite corner there
was another door: and at the back part were
out-buildings rising sharply up the hill behind.
At the ends of the hall under the gables were great
arks and kists against the wall, and at one end the
aforesaid loom: but along the side were hung the
men's weapons, spears and shields and coats of
mail, and their hunting and fishing tackle, well out
of the way in a row beneath the row of windows,
and over long benches that lined the hall on either
hand.

In the middle of the benches were two high
seats, one on this side and one on that over against
it. They were like the great elbow-chairs
or settles you see in old farm-houses; roomy
enough for three, carved on their high backs,
and with carved heads to their posts in front.
The children had a tale that one head was father
and one was mother: older folk would say the
figures stood for Odin and Freya. Anyway
they were something more than just ornaments;
they gave a holiness to the place, and made the
high seat of the master as it were a kind of
temple-stall.

Before the benches on one side of the hall

stood a long table, all of oak, like the seats and the wainscotting and the rest, brown already with age and bright with rubbing : but on the other side the tables had been taken off their trestles and laid up to make more room, and because half their men were abroad with Swein at sea. On this side sat Unna in her own high seat with the cradle at her feet, and before her the hearth with its thin smoke going up, and the sun-ray striking through it, and blazing in the fern that was strewed on the floor. And when the sun-spot crept upon the cradle she stooped down and moved it a little backwards, so that the bright light should not wake the baby. And when he stirred she pushed the cradle with her foot and sang again while she sewed at his shirt. And the loom went clattering on with the steady noise that is good for babies' slumber. Nothing else was heard, except the birds singing in the green-wood around, and far-away clamour of people working in the fields.

When the baby was sound asleep again, Unna rose, and walked softly to see where his brothers might be : and her gown trained on the ferny floor. She stood in the porch and called, but not too loudly, "Ho! Orm! Hundi! where are you ? what are you doing ?"

But they were off. And so she sat down again and sewed till her eyelids were heavy with the warmth and the dimness of the place.

"Eh, barn," she said, "what makes one so

drowsy? Sleep by day and starve at night, they used to say."

"Most like a stranger is coming," said the old woman from the loom. For it was thought that a man's fetch went before and brought slumber.

"Few strangers here but bad ones," said Unna.

"May be it's the master and the men."

"Why, they are gone but these three weeks, and who knows when they may come back, and how? And it's weary waiting, and a deal on one's hands: let alone the chances of raid and robbery."

"What, there's Raud thy brother and all," said the old woman sharply. "And folk must live. It would be ill liked if the master never brought home an armful of finery, or another hand or so for the farm, or a barrel of somewhat sharper than we can brew."

"Aye, its a lone spot: not that I complain: for Raud is a handy lad. It will be a bad day when he takes land upbank, as he talks of doing."

"Nay, never heed his talk. He must light on some one fit first," answered the weaver: "and how will he do that hereaway, I'd like to know? As for thy man, and my man, and the rest, they are men, with hands to their elbows and heads on their shoulders."

"Or had, you may say, to start with," said Unna with a sigh.

" Heads, aye, and know their ways about. Look at my old man. These forty winters he has come back to me the same as ever."

" Aye, he has a cat's life, has old Toli."

" Not so old as that comes to, neither," said the crone. " And thankful we should be for our good men and for a good roof over us. Eh, child, when I think on all we have come through."

" No fells, no dales," said she : " no loom, no clatter ; " but she hastened to add " I am out of sorts to-day. There's overmuch to be done before they come, to redd all up for the back end. There's yon window now. I wonder if the ladder is handy. One might do it oneself sooner than bide for those lazy carles." And she got up and walked uneasily to the door again.

" Nay barn, let it be : its none of thy job," said the old woman ; muttering to her loom, for there was nobody else to hear. " The mistress is queer and fidgetty to-day. One might think somewhat was going to happen."

But the ladder was up against a rick in the distance, and men were on it, thatching and shouting. Over the water, and all round, wooded hills shook in the heat-haze. Unna shaded her eyes and looked once more for Orm and Hundi, but nought she spied. She came back and sat on a stool against her high-seat, and tried to sew. But the sun-spot crept on to her lap, like some little wounded animal, dragging itself painfully to refuge there. It shone through her work, and through her fingers, so that they seemed blood-red: and it dived into the red stone in her ring, and made it redder than blood: and it burned on the gold like the whole sun itself, a blaze of mystery, a dream of glory.

Clitter-clatter went on the loom. " Poor soul," said the old woman : " best thing she can do "— as she saw Unna's tired head sink back against the post of the high-seat, and her long white throat slide out of the white neckerchief, and her chin heaved up, like a blown wild rose leaf, warm in the reflected sunshine.

Then in the stillness the sun-spot dragged itself off her hand and off her lap, and tumbled to the floor again in one roundel, just like a bubble that gathers itself together in the dark pool under a waterfall, out of the shattering of the spray : a dream of death.

Clitter-clatter went on the loom nevertheless : and the birds sang still in the green world outside. The mother's dreams were soft and sweet, of life's love, and life's labour, that never fail nor come to bitterness ; for these regard not glory, and fear not death.

## CHAPTER III

## SWEIN'S HOME-COMING

Now we leave Mistress Unna and baby Thorstein asleep, to tell about Orm and Hundi and how they floated boats. Those boys had run off to the workshop where smithying was done, and found a heap of chips and shavings, and made each of them a boat, with a thin shaving for a sail : and of course they must away to the beck, as nobody was there to shout after them. So they ran over the cobble-paved garth between the byres, and out at the gate of the turf wall that stood round about the " town." Then they were at the boat-landing, among planks and rollers, ropes and chains, and the delicious smell of tar that hung about the boat building sheds, and reeked in the hot sunshine.

The shore was steep, and shelving into a dub just there : so they ran downbank towards the flats that open out below the point. Under the crags and fir-trees of the nab they had to scramble over rocks and stones, and to splash through salt pools left by the outgoing tide : but soon they came to a stretch of rippled sand between fell and firth, and waded a beck that flowed from the woods and wound north-ward along their edge to join the Leven.

" Ha ! " said Orm, " now we are on my fairy

island. It is all gold, and yon side the beck runs down, and yon side the beck runs up. Now we are on my holm, and I will fight thee for thy boat."

For it was a custom among these Northmen when two had a quarrel to go upon an island and fight it out. So Orm beat Hundi, and ran off with both the boats and pushed them from the shore until they sailed down-bank with the tide. There was no one to cry for, so Hundi held his peace : he brushed his eyes with his hand and pattered on, his bare feet crisping the soppy sand ripples, and leaving their prints in a chain of little tarns. And when he came to the next bend in the river, lo and behold his own boat came straight to shore and into his hands, while the boat that Orm had made was rocking in mid-channel with its sail draggled in the water. Orm began to throw handfuls of sand over it, to draw it in : and while they were intent upon this job and keeping no look out, suddenly they heard shouts not far off, and the clash of oars, and a great craft swung round into that reach and bore straight down upon the chip boat. A moment they stood dumbfoundered, and then turned and ran for the woods like young rabbits. For in those days it was no idle threat when mothers said to truant boys, " Mind you don't go out of sight, for fear a man catches you."

But just when the throb began to beat very hard in their throats, and they were stopped by the steep crumbling banks of the little beck that

bounded the holm, they heard, like a shepherd
calling sheep, " Ho, Orm! ho, Hundi! ho!"
and they turned and looked: and then looked
at one another with bright eyes and panting
too much to laugh. They set off running back to
the ship, which they knew well enough now.
The rowers had eased and brought her close to
the edge of the sandbank: and that could well be
done, for she drew very little water and was nigh
flat bottomed. Swein, with a brown square
face, and bushy fair beard, and bright blue eyes
laughing out of the locks of his tawny hair, came
wading ashore. He caught up one child under
each arm, waded out again, and hoisted them to
hands aboard. Then catching at the gunwale
near the steering oar, he raised himself half-
length and vaulted over. The water dripped
from his gartered hose and blue kirtle skirts:
for his mail-coat was doffed, and he wore only
a belted kirtle or blouse over his white linen
sark.

" Eh, father, mother will snape thee for getting
of thyself in a mess!" said Hundi compassionately.
" But never heed her: I'll say it was to fetch us
aboard."

" But my dragon is wrecked," grumbled Orm.

" And is that all you have to say to your old
father when he comes home?"

" Nay," said Orm looking round coolly, " What
have ye brought me?"

" No great things, barn, this trip," said Swein,
with half a smile, as he took the steering oar.

"Now then, lads, all's well, by this token. The barns say little, but there is enough of it, and enow of them. Forward all now : a spurt to finish our day's work. Lift her ! here she goes. Lift her ! "

A dozen of long blades, six aside, with a couple of men at each, churned the sandy shallows, as the boat swept round the curve and up stream. Long in the keel and low in the board she was, with swinging curves at stem and stern rising swan-like to the figure-head and the carved stern-post. But the ugly mask of a spit-fire dragon was taken off the bows, now that they were so near home ; for it was a belief among these people that the land-wights, the good fairies and useful brownies, would be scared by such a sight, or at least take it in dudgeon, and depart. So the figure-head had a good face for home waters, and a hideous one to put on when they got out to sea and to work among strangers. The gunwales were notched into dog-tooth markings and what old wives call box-pattern in their quiltings. The strong upstanding tholes were curiously carved with knots and worm-twists. Great oars were lashed to these tholes and the rowers stood to their work and pushed the handles. There was a step for a mast forward, but the mast and yard were lying along the gangway that ran between the ranks of rowers, from the decked forecastle to the quarter deck ; and the sail, useless to-day, was wrapped about the spars. There was little else to be seen : the few bales or chests she might carry were stowed, and her decks were clear, as if at any moment she might meet with an enemy. Over the gunwale hung the men's shields, a dozen aside, each by its strap from its own pin, and ready to be caught up in the twinkling of an eye. Black and gold they were painted for the most part, and if one was more black then the next was more golden, so they made a fine show from without.

Every man aboard was a sturdy fellow, who would go through with it, whatever he took in hand ; bronzed with the sun and great-thewed with downright hard work. Some of them were Swein's own Northmen from the Isle of Man, old comrades and followers of former days : some were Welsh of the country, his bought servants ; but trusty men under a good leader. They were all his house-mates, or lived in cots of their own hard by.

So now that they were near home they laid to with a will. The children played helping father with the steering sweep, which knocked them over every time it was put up or down. Swein gave the stroke faster and faster as the landing place came in sight, with his " Lift her ! " and they made her spin up the last reach. Round she went, and half-way up the bank ploughing the sand. Orm and Hundi tumbled on the decks laughing. Then out men leapt, and ran her up on her rollers above high-water mark, as they were used with these light flat-bottomed craft. The easier it was, for by now they were spied and recognised from the fields, and a dozen farm servants had run down to lend a hand.

You may be sure it was merry-night that evening at Greenodd, and Unna was wide awake and bustling to make amends for her laziness, as she called it. The servant lasses had a busy time, with the fire to stoke, and the supper to cook, and the tables to set. Meanwhile the men went to their bath in the bath-house, and shifted their sea-clothes. Long before the sun sank behind the high fell at the back of the house they were sitting at meat, cooled and ravenous, on the long hall-benches, behind heaps of barley cake and haver-bread, and dried fish; great bowls of broth and porridge into which many spoons were dipped at once : and platters of butter and cheese and curds, and trenches piled with steaks, which they ate with their sheath-knives : and it may be said for them that if some eat foully with forks, others, to the manner bred, can eat fairly with fingers. As to drinking, the lasses had their work in running to and fro with ale and buttermilk, to slocken thirsty men who had rowed from Carnforth since breakfast on a broiling hot day.

## CHAPTER IV

## ON THE HOWE

SWEIN was in his own high seat, and while the din lasted ate like another, looking now and then but shyly through the hearth-smoke at Unna over against him. At last " Eat, Unna ! " he cried, " and take thy supper. One would think I was a merman, and stared at for a show. Sup thy porridge, lass, and be hearty."

" I have supped," she said, " and supped well."

" Supped with her eyes," said old Toli, for here he was, holding out his empty horn. " A dry supper, but a big one."

" I've seen her eat nought," said Swein. " What has she supped on ? "

" Thee," said Toli. " Eh, Mistress ? "

But Unna, though she was used to the uncourtly ways of her own folk and could laugh at a rough jest, was less at ease than she had hoped to be. When the meal began, she had looked lovingly across at her man, making out his features one by one through the dimness and the smoke, watching for the open smile that he was used to give her, on such nights as these of home-coming, when his first hunger was stayed and the feasting was forward : the free smile and friendly nod that signalled all's well. But this time it was long in coming: and she got only the half glances and the rough and puzzling "Eat, child." Her eyes filled with tears, and her mind flew to chances of mishap. There were all the men back, and no wounds to be seen: the ship was safe: what could it be? Some woman in the case. What else? And her quick wit, wrong for once, revealed to her, like a lightning flash, a whole story of dismay.

Men were fed by now, and they drank healths, first to Odin for the kinsfolk, and then to Niord and Frey for peace and plenty. When they were come to the cup for Bragi—he was the god of talking and of tale-telling and song—it was Swein's old use and wont to begin the story of his doings and travellings since the last farewell, and to hold them all till midnight wrapt in the tale. This time he put down the horn untasted: and when they waited for him in wonder, suddenly hushed, he thrust the table from him, and went forth.

Unna looked at Raud her brother who sat by her, signing with her eyes as much as to say "What now?" and the sign he gave her was a nod toward the door.

"Aye, mistress," said Toli, "till him, and wheedle him back. To think of folk leaving good ale for an idle whim."

"What then?" she said, flashing back at him, while Raud made room for her.

"Nought that matters: nay, never ask me."

With a beating heart she went through the porch, and her knees trembled as she passed. Swein was

c

going slowly through the gate, slackening his pace, though he neither turned nor looked; but yet it seemed as if he wanted to be overtaken.

There is a steep path up the cliffs a little to the seaward of the houses, mounting rapidly at first over the crags by rude steps in the rock, and then through the great rough stems of ancient fir-trees, and between thickets of blackberry-brambles, until it comes out upon a clear space on the top. It is not so far that one need halt to take breath by the way, and yet lofty enough for the eye to sweep north, south, east and west, down the firth and up the valley, and across to the far-away fells.

This was Swein's howe, where he went daily and often-times a day, to watch the bright line of the sea, if by chance a sail might be made out, friend or foe or merchant vessel cruising round the coast. There also he could overlook his land; for the acres of oats and barley and the hay-fields lay close beneath, around the mouth of the Crake. His own summer pastures were on the fells hard by, and his swine fed in the woods around. He could see what was doing, and what was left undone, from that howe: count men and beasts, and hear the sounds of work going on in smithy or shed. Here he would take counsel with himself about new dealings with this man and that, and lay his plans and dream over his enterprises. And when there was trouble or when things went aslew, it was on this howe that he sat to wrestle with his thoughts. And it was his mind when he should be dead to be buried there and look out from his grave upon his children and his home, and the kind land that had given him a resting-place from his wanderings.

He sat down upon the turf seat on the top, and Unna, who had tripped lightly after him, sat down alongside. He rested both elbows on his knees as one ashamed to speak, but moved not away. What can it be ? was her thought.

For now the sun was set in the gold half of the sky, and the other half was clear pansy coloured, with a round moon rising through the fringe of dusky woods. Below them the tide was flowing in, and the wash of it was heard in the stillness : the great rings and bows of the river in front swung about and along over the silvery flats, like the track of a skater on ice. And against the northern glow far away, sharp violet ridges of distant mountain stood around them, serene, above the tumbling forest and rich promontories of Crake and Leven.

Then she slid her arm over his shoulder, and her fingers twitched at the brooch that fastened his cloak ; and it seemed that he was her man still. The moon had disentangled itself at last, and began to glimmer on the tide ripple. " Twilight brings talk," thought Unna, and waited for him to begin.

## CHAPTER V

## THE KING'S MOTE

" WELL, wife," said Swein at last, " I am trapped, seemingly. It is stand and deliver, is it ? What, there is nothing so dreadful after all, turn and turn it over as one may. But that is yet to be judged : I suppose I must put my case, and tell my story.

" How we set off I need not tell. We came to Carnforth, and there we met most of our neighbours from the country-side. There was Arnolf and his people from Arnolfsby in Dunnerdale: there were Raven and Ulfar from this side of Furness : Ulf and Arni from up the Kent ; and Hawk was there on the spot, for he lives hard by, and it was his folk looked after the ships of us that came by water ; and other friends from over the sands. We took counsel together, and agreed that being summoned to this meeting, be it peace or war, we should go : but that we should keep together and make one band, for it is ill dealing with folk that are neither kith nor kin.

" Thou knowest, Unna, that we reckoned this bit of land was no man's land until we came and took it. Northward beyond the fells the Welsh hold themselves under the rule of their own king : but never did I hear of his coming into these parts or having a power on Furness coasts. Across there in Cartmel they say they belong to the minster priests and be no king's men at all : and beyond that again, if Ragnar Lodbrog's sons did ever take the land, neither Angle nor Dane in Kentdale or Lunesdale has paid shot to York for many a year.

" ' Fifty years ago, after Halfdan sacked Carlisle and laid all these parts under him, and began to settle them from the eastward, then, I grant you,' says one of us, ' this would be in the Dane-law : but now that king Halfdan is dead and all the kings that came after him and there is no law in York, why, look you, we owe them nothing, and need but keep together,' says he, ' to be our own men like the Icelanders.' And this talk we held to be but fair and good, and took hands all round upon it.

" So we got horses at the bank where the old road meets the sands, and came to a burg called Lancaster where we had to meet the main part of the host from the north. The burgers gave us what we wanted with little ado : a handful of chapmen and cowpers who trade with travellers on the great highway. But I thought they grinned a little when we talked of going against the Saxons.

" Well, in a day or so there is a great trumpeting and booming, and up comes Constantine the Scots' king, and his brother Donal the Welsh King, and among them Ketel and others of our own men from Cumberland, and some from Galloway : and it was hail fellow with many an old friend.

" ' It seems we are but short-handed,' said Hawk : ' or is the Saxon king of less account than we reckon for ? '

" With that they laughed outright, and the cat came out of the bag, tail and all : for they told us flatly that there was no fighting to be thought of : but only a great meeting of all the people in Britain under their kings and earls.

" ' And pray what king do you reckon us to be under ? ' said I to Ketel.

" ' Well,' said Ketel, ' Donal flatters himself because I have taken up my abode in his borders, that I am his man. I remember well, when I met him first, what a wagging of beards there was. Some were for hunting us out, at which the old whiteheads turned pale, though I made as if I understood none of their chatter. By and by the whitest beard of all made a terrible long-winded speech, setting forth how, if they turned us out, there would be swarms more of us revenging ourselves upon them : and how there was land enough and to spare on the holms and flats by Dundraw : and how, when we Northmen were let alone we were decent merchants, buying goods and servants. He said we always had plenty of money and brought trade to the country-side : and he wound up in a flowery way, I could understand him well :—Look you, says he, waving his old skinny arms about. These white strangers (for they call us white, and the Danes black, and right they are to my thinking) these strangers, says he, will be a soft bolster to our heads. When hard knocks come, they will get them, and we shall feel the less. So they blethered and clattered like crows, and in the end let us be : and here we are ! '

" ' Well, Ketel Bolster,' said I—eh, how they did laugh—' if Donal suits thee for lord and master, he suits not me.' At which Ketel would at me, and I would have beaten him well, only they stood in and stopped us.

" Next day we trotted along the great high road. It's a strange thing, Unna, that folk ever took the trouble to heap hard stones together for nought but to walk on. But there it goes up hill and down dale, through bog and brink ; and evenly built with cobbles and grit for all the world like a great long hearth-spot, and as straight as an arrow-flight. They told me it was folk from Romeburg that built it : though what they could have done it for, I know nought : unless it were a priest's trick to mark out the Church gate. Anyhow it was hard riding clitter-clatter on the stones all day long : I had rather have galloped over the green grass : but keep together was the word, for there were but few of us, and with such a pack of Welsh and Scots before and behind, one never knows what may happen.

" The next night we harboured at a spot they called Ribblechester, and the next at Manchester, which is a pretty place and one would have thought a strong work enough to hold against any comers : but the Saxons took it last summer from those lubberly Danes. I fell in talk with the goodman where they lodged us, and it seemed that not only they in Manchester, but all the Danelaw, had got a thorough fright of the Marchmen and the Saxons, and they were hastening to this meeting like thralls to supper, each afraid to be last man in.

" ' And who are *they* ? ' say I.

" ' Why,' says he, ' everybody of account, but in especial the new king of York.'

" ' New king ? ' say I.

" ' Aye,' says he : ' Ragnwald Ivarson.'

" ' What ! ' say I ; ' Ragnwald, the rascal, he was at Waterford but a while since : what is he doing here ? '

" ' Why,' says he, ' where in the round world is thy den, man or mountain bear ? '

" ' Softly,' say I : ' Swain is my name and Bear's son is my breeding. Swain's fist or bear's paw, which wilt have ? '

" ' No offence, guest,' says he : ' But I thought every one knew that Ragnwald was kicked out of Waterford—'

" ' Well done,' say I.

" ' And killed the old king's earls but a few months since, and marched into York.'

" ' Marched into hell ! ' said I.

" ' No such thing : the tale was that he died three years ago ; but there he is, and thou wilt see him at the king's mote, for he will be there to make his peace with Eadward and be confirmed in his kingdom.'

" ' He shall see me,' said I, ' and get more peace than he wots of.' For Unna, never a day passes but I think of that fight off Man, and our good

Bardi's ship going down with the Dane's iron beak through her ribs.

" Well, this last day we rode over fells they called Peak to Bakewell, and if it was forecast at Manchester, here was sooth. Hardly were we within sight of the place, but a flock of horsemen comes spurring out to meet us, and after some parley makes a lane for us to pass through, one by one, like sheep counted into a fold : and of each a jack-in-office asks name and nation and so forth before he may go his ways. And when we come among the houses, which were as thick as trees in a wood, we must halt till we are told off to our lodgings : and there we must bide till it please my lord the Saxon king to see us. Not but that we were well bestowed for bed and board : and to see the sights was something. Houses, I say, for ever, and nigh upon all of them new built or even in the building. Strangers from all parts of the land ; why, from all the round world it seemed. And all day and every day market in the lanes and open places, and wares to be bought the like of which I never saw, not even on Dublin strand when the fleet comes in. What little I had of silver in my bag soon went : but it passed the time to chaffer and turn the wares over. I got a bit of a scarf : the cowper said it came from Micklegarth and maybe beyond : even he was all the way from Londonburg. I paid a pretty penny for it, and yet thought I was making a good bargain. Mayhappen you will shake your head : but don it first. There are two or three trifles beside in a kist the lads will bring up and we can unpack to-morrow.

"All this while no Ragnwald was to be seen, and I began to reckon nought of the Manchester man's tale. At last comes jack-in-office, and bids us to the Saxon king: and in we go, over a bridge and through a gate in the stout oaken wall new cut: and there is a yard in the midst, full of his house-carles, and one could not but see with half an eye that they were big fellows and their weapons were of the best.

"I need not tell thee, Unna, what a king's house is like: but this burg was a sight to see, for its bigness without and within for its hangings and carvings and gold and silver: yet most of all the king we have heard tell about sitting on his high seat, all gold, with his high crown and gold staff: and his earls and priests in gold cloaks and horned caps, holding their crooks like so many warlocks: and indeed who knows what spell they were casting over us? Anyhow there were Constantine and Donal down on their knees, like men bewitched, and their hands in the king's hands, saying after one that stood by—'I Constantine, and I Donal, take thee Eadward to be my father and lord, and father and lord of all my folk.' And then came Ealdred Eadulfson of Bamborough, with his Angles, and did likewise. And then came Ragn-wald.

"Unna, lass, I was mad wrath when I saw him, and I could have run upon him there: only Hawk held me by one arm and Ketel by the other, and said 'Peace, man, at a mote!' And then stood

one forth in the silence, and spoke, ' Forasmuch as
you have commended you to our king Eadward,
king of Angles and Saxons, and overlord of
Cornwall and of Gwynedd and of all the West
Welsh, to be his men, each and all of you—'

" ' Nay, not I,' cried a voice : they said it was
mine, though I knew not I spoke, for I was that
angry. But you may guess if there was a haybay
and swords drawn. They plucked me by the
sleeve and shouted in my ears ' Peace man, peace ! '
I tried to get at my sword, and looked for Ragnwald first. But the Saxon king sat still on his high
seat, and waved his wand, and men were quiet
again and I standing thrust out in the midst.

" ' Come hither, good friend,' he said, speaking
very fair and slowly, so that I could understand
him well, for the Saxon tongue is hard to hear at
first : ' Come nigh and tell me what ails thee.'

" And I marched up to the high seat, and said I,
' Nothing but this, king ; that I have sworn
nought to thee : and I see my enemy standing
there.'

" ' Softly, good man,' says the king ; ' this is a
hallowed mote : if all foes here were to fight, we
should eat each other up.' And he smiled, Unna,
and I could not but laugh too, for I thought of yon
Irish cats thy mother used to tell of.

" ' And who is thy foe ? ' says Eadward.

" ' Ragnwald Ivarson.'

" With that, out steps Ragnwald as proud as a
peacock.

" ' I never set eyes on the carle,' says he.

" ' But I know thee, Ragnwald,' said I; ' and well I mind the day when thy ship ran Bardi's down, ten years ago, off Man.'

" ' And is that all ? ' said he.

" ' Come,' said Eadward the King : ' this day we let bygones be bygones. Have I nothing against Ragnwald, thinkst thou ? and were Bardi Ottarson's folk sackless of scathe to me and mine ? Who art thou, good fellow, and whence ? '

" So I told him my name and where I lived : and the upshot of it was that Eadward says, ' Well then, if I let thee dwell there in peace, wilt thou leave thy neighbours in peace ? '

" What could one say but Aye ?

" Now, all this while was the high priest muttering and making signs at me, and doubtless I was bewitched. For I looked in the king's eyes and clean forgot about Ragnwald, and all the mind I had to live and die my own man, and no king's man. The people in the hall seemed to be a dream, and there were I and Eadward only. He reached out his hand to me, and my hand was in his, and the ring fell from his arm upon mine. ' Kneel, man, kneel ! ' cried the bystanders : but Eadward smiled, like one who has mated you at chess.

" ' Take hands on a bargain,' he said : ' that is the Northman's way, is it not ? Nay, keep the ring, friend Swein.'

" And there it is," said Swein : casting a gold armlet on the turf. " The bull's snout-ring, I call it : the thrall's collar."

" And is that the tale ? " said Unna, stooping to

pick it up. "Oh, man! serve the best and spurn the worst. I am weary of this wandering and warring; I would fain end our days as this day ends."

And the moon cast a great stream of light along the Leven.

"I thought there could be no welcome for a nithing like me."

"Welcome?" she said. "Thrice welcome for the best tale of these ten years: a thousand welcomes if the peace but hold good."

"Maybe through the winter," said Swein, as they rose to leave the howe. Then, as their feet brushed through the beaded dew, "I doubt if the oath will bind us long," said he. "Methought when he took mine, that I was holding a dead man's hand."

## CHAPTER VI

### OF FURNESS FOLK A THOUSAND
### YEARS SINCE

THE winter wore and the summer came: and
Eadward still ruled the land in peace. But about
hay-harvest there were rumours, at which Swein
nodded to his wife as one who says " You see I was
right." And when haytime was well passed, came
people from over the fell bidding him to a meeting
at Ulfar's Lund.

Now this Ulfar of whom we spoke before, had
land on the brink of the fells where they met the
low country, about an hour's journey to the
southward of Greenodd. He was an old man, and
he had been a chieftain formerly, and was a man of
worth even now, and a stickler for old times and
the old laws.

Near his " town " (as we still call hereabouts any
cluster of dwellings though it be nothing like a
city) and between it and the waterside, there was a
broad mound, not so high, but standing by itself :
from which could be seen a great ring of country all
around : across the firth, Cark and Cartmel way,
and all the Sandgate, that is the road across the
sands of Leven, and whosoever was coming and
going, for good or ill : and down the coast to

Conishead, that was the king's seat, where the
York kings had their folk to take tax of the iron-
workers and mines : and then again westward
over the black moor, Swarthmoor, to Orgrave and
the iron-mines.

When the Northmen came into Hougun, that
is the country we call Furness, they found a few
English and some Welsh here and there. There
were Welsh in the low land over against Walney,
and Rhos they called the meadow-land thereabouts.
There were already villages between that and
Dalton and up to Broughton on the Duddon, and
churches there, and priests, no doubt ; but such as
heard little of any English bishops, or what we
should call government whether of church or state.
Across at Cartmel the land and all the Welsh that
were on it had long ago been given to St. Cuthbert's
Minster ; but Furness was a bit of that broad
debatable ground over which the tide of invasion
flowed from age to age and ebbed back again, just
like the sea upon Morecambe shores. As time
went on, here a piece of sand was fully reclaimed,
and there a piece of land was swallowed up.

But when the Northmen came they took the
snuggest places for shelter and for safety. They
always wanted a good landing spot for their flat-
bottomed boats, so that when summer came,
between sheep-shearing and corn-harvest, they
might make use of their spare time by pushing out
to sea and doing a little quiet trade, or may be at
times you might call it " raid," up and down the
coasts of the Irish Sea. And so they went on

farming and seafaring, turn about, and picked up a better living the harder they worked at both.

Of all the Northmen in Furness our tale tells that Ulfar was the chief. Being as we said a stickler for the old laws, Ulfar made a sacrificing place on that mound near his town among the trees that grew upon it. He set up an altar to worship Thor in that grove, which the Northmen called Lund. To the feasts of the Lund he bade his neighbours; and they were glad to come, not only for the worship, and to be on good terms with the gods, but because there was a chance of meeting one another, and talking over their affairs. So many came and so long they stayed, as folk who had a good way to travel and were loth to return in a hurry, that around about the Lund they built booths to lodge in, and set up tents. Some brought wares to sell, and others started games and wrestling-matches: so that it was quite like a fair, at the great feasts after Yule and after sheep-shearing, and after corn-harvest.

So, as summer was passing, Swein was bidden to a feast: he took boat and landed at the Hummer-side and went up to the Lund. There men were all talking of the new king, and what should be done about him. For Eadward was now dead and Athelstan his son reigned in his stead; a stirring man, and not one to let the fire smoulder under his feet. The news was that Sigtrygg of York—Sihtric he is called by the English—had marched out as soon as the old king was gone: but Athelstan was before-hand, and met him at Tamworth in the

March, and there they made peace, and Athelstan gave Sigtrygg his sister Eathgita to wife, and confirmed him in his kingdom.

"And Ragnwald the viking, what of him?" asked Swein.

Nobody knew: some said he was gone to France, some said he was killed: anyway he was out of the road by this time, and Sigtrygg was now head king over all the Danelaw. These great kings being at peace there was no longer any chance of a rising: not that it mattered much to the Northmen hereabouts: but they were all good fighting men as well as good farmers and merchants. A summer without war was a season lost, to their way of thinking. So they went home again grumbling; and the next winter nothing happened, but that at Greenodd, Thorstein grew too big for his cradle, and began to walk and talk.

D

# CHAPTER VII

## COWPERS' CRACKS

### (The great Aurora of A.D. 926)

EVENING it was, when the afternoons were already beginning to lengthen, but before the frost was over. Thorstein came running in at his bedtime, and " Mother, mother," says he, " the fell's afire ! "

Sure enough there was a sight to make the boldest heart shake in its step like a ricketty mast. For it seemed that all the heavens were aflame; as though, beyond the high hills, woods and forests— nay, the very mountains themselves were blazing in a bright glow. And one while, great sheets of wavering flame turned blood-colour, and the sky between them was green, and the stars faded away. Then it throbbed, and shifted, and changed like clouds of sunset, though the sun was long gone down and there was no moon. Swein and Raud and the rest of them were aught but cowards ; but when they turned in, they saw one another pale as grass in the firelight, and laughed but little that night. But what it might mean they disputed among themselves : and it was mostly thought there would be bloodshed wherever that blood in the sky had shone.

There was another evening soon after, when trading merchants came in a boat up the firth of the Leven. Such were never unwelcome in winter, when folk were at home, and work was slack; there was time to rummage the wares and hear the news. These cowpers also found the coast a deal safer when no summer fighting was going on. As for storms, they were never out of sight of a shelter, creeping about the shore, picking up what they could, and always well entertained. They had come last from Cowpran, which was their market-place with the Cartmel Welsh, where the old road met the Sandgate over the Leven. Greenodd was the only house up the firth, and it was not always that chapmen called there; and so they were made much of.

When they had got their packs up to the house, and when they had been served and suppered, out came news. For it seems that Sigtrygg had died, not long after that great fire-flaught in the heavens. "Aye," said the cowpers, "you may well cock your ears: others beside you guessed that great doings would happen. But listen now, Swein Biornson and all.

"Folk said there was foul play in that matter: and Sigtrygg's sons by the queen that was, the Irish-woman, charged it on the queen that is, the English-woman for whose sake the king had taken christening: but having won her, he went back on his word and took to sacrificing again. Upon which off she goes to her brother Athelstan, wed and yet unwed, as one may say. And then dies

Sigtrygg. Athelstan, they say, knew as much about it as another : but that is only guess work, and neither here nor there. Anyhow he is a brisk lad and sprack, not the man to see his sister put upon, right or wrong. Away he marches with a great power to York ; and no sooner is he in sight, but Sigtrygg's sons show him their heels, the best way they could : and that was out by the back door, and away up the big North road, across the fells, till they come to Penrith in Cumberland : and there we lose sight of them. But they do say that Guthferth Sigtryggson started on the North road to visit Constantine king of Scots, and get shelter with him if he could : and Olaf Cuaran said good-bye to his brother and went west, as if to seek his uncle Guthferth, who is king now in Dublin. The question is What next ? for you may be sure they will not rest, and the Irish and Scots will be glad of a chance for a throw at the young king—the king of all England as he will reckon himself."

" And so that bad business at Bakewell comes to nothing ? " said Swein. " I knew as much. But this lad Athelstan, by what you tell of him must be a fine cockerel to crow so loud. And now I call to mind, he must have been the youngster that sat on the high-seat step at Bakewell : he with the bright eyes."

" Aye," said the chapman, " tall and slender : he would be some thirty winters old when you saw him : handsome and flaxenhaired : and ye will have noticed how his hair was all twisted up with gold threads. He's a real king to look at, though they say he is but the son of a shepherd lass whom Eadward his father lighted upon in his travels. And he is a good sort, they say, and has seen the world, and knows better than most kings how folk live. Why, he speaks our language like one of us, and has done a bit of seafaring. But for all that he is a Saxon, and he must stand by his own kin."

" Well, what are we to do ? Knock him on the head ? "

" To hold thy peace," said Unna, " is my advice : and watch the weather."

" A wise woman is my wife," said Swein, " and knows the weasel's trick. After all, we are free of our oath, and need not put our heads into the snare again."

" Laugh at the lightning when the storm has passed," said the chapmen. " Athelstan with his power was at York awhile since, and may be in Lunesdale by now to foreset us."

" Let him come ! " shouted Swein : " and hey, for a gradely good stir-about, and pot luck for the sharpest claws ! "

" Look you, master cowper, and all the rest," said Unna, " if you set up for eggbattles and put my man on shouting, I shall have those blessed barns awake and on my hands all night. Swein Biornson is a good friend to all his friends but himself alone. We have seen a little fighting, to our sorrow : and the talk of the trade hangs about the tongue, like smoke in a half-burnt house. But here we are, and here we stay if we can. As for Swein, his bark is

worse than his bite. He shaped well for a good
farmer in Man before Ragnwald shifted us : and he
shapes well for a good farmer now : and pity it
were if we be plucked up by the roots again.
These great kings and their powers come not where
nothing is to be had but kale pottage and hard bats.
I'll uphold it, Athelstan will be bound for the great
burgs in the north, or connily on his way home
again. And I should reckon it ill done of you
good fellows to go abroad stirring up useless riot,
or coming hither to entrap quiet folk into rash
vows."

So the cowpers said they were but giving the
news and meant no harm : and that it never had
been their way to go talebearing and raising
strife, nor never would be. At which Unna
smiled, and got up to make them beds before
the fire on the benches of the hall. When she
saw them well furnished with rugs to hap them
and bolsters for their heads, she sent her folk to
their chambers ; put her knitting away into a
basket ; lit a rushlight in an iron candlestick ; and
bade them good-night.

Child Thorstein was fast asleep on the farther
side of the bolster in the narrow chamber of
their lock-bed, with one little dimpled arm stretched
upon the quilted coverlet. Swein, sitting upon a
kist to unlace his shoes, looked sleepily at him,
and then at her, as she let a sheaf of yellow hair fall
upon her white nightsark : and the rushlight on
the shelf shone down through it, flickering in the
draught from the little round window above : for

the lock-bed was just like a cabin aboard ship.

"Right thou art, Irish fairy," said he: "and always right. But ah, you women, you never felt the heartiness of a good fight."

"Nay, we are nought: that's well known," she laughed, drawing the curtain round the baby. "Bar the door, Norse bearsark."

## CHAPTER VIII

## THE GIANT COMES IN

RESTLESS they were that spring; and Unna was anxious and somewhat pettish when Swein talked over the chances of a war. For one good thing, however, he was eager to get forward with work at home, so that he might leave the place well redd up: and that pleased the mistress right well. So they put on until haytime, which is pretty early in the low fields by the waterside, and these were all they had under hay : for the summer-pastures on the fell were hardly stubbed, and far too stony for cutting with the ley.

Well, they were all raking by the beck side, and the mistress was pouring ale to slocken them, and the boys were tumbling in the haycocks, when there was a terrible stir in the woods on the other bank. These woods were on a long hill that made a wall to the valley over against Greenodd : and the fields lay between, and the tide ran up the Crake to where the valley narrowed and the fields ended, and there was a wath or fording-place. Dogs barked, and men shouted, and swine squealed. They could see by the shaking of the boughs that something was going forward : most like a wild-cat hunt, they said to one another, and left it to the swine-herds to deal with.

But presently there was a great splash in the ford, and out came a most enormous man, half naked, with long red hair and red beard. He held one hand on high, carrying they could not see what. In his other hand was a huge ugly stock of tree. All the swineherds' dogs were after him, and the men too, for that matter : but he made no account of them, until one dog leaped at his legs as he came up the bank on the hither side. The big man turned and flicked him like a football, high in the air and splash in the water : and ran straight for Greenodd garth.

Swein and his men ran up to meet him with their rakes and forks, less afraid than puzzled. The big man never stayed until he came to the door, and then he thrust the thing he was carrying into a chink of the posts, and began talking in a strange tongue. He was indeed a giant, head and shoulders taller than any of the Greenodd men, but of quite another make : crane-legged and clumsy handed and jolter-headed ; unlike Swein, who was no little fellow though his strength was rather in the breadth of his shoulders and the ropy sinews of his wrist and forearm, like a seafaring man as he had been bred. They saw that the thing he had brought was a burnt splinter, and they knew that it was a war-arrow and token of fighting : but whence or why they could not guess. Presently came Unna ; and listening to the man's talk, she smiled, and began to answer him. The creature made her a low court-reverence, half haughty, half awkward, and spoke to her with a strutting way about him, like a cock upon pattens, as one may say.

When he had done, " Friends," she said, " this man's talk is like the talk of our thralls, and I gather thus much of his discourse, that he is the messenger of a war-rising in the north. He bids you to a weapon-show beyond the fells, you and all the country-side, whoever will cast in his lot against the Saxon king. And you are to send on the arrow to our next neighbours, and bid them likewise."

" Speer of him, Unna, where and when," said Swein.

So she asked him, and said his story was to the intent that he would come again in ten days' time to lead them over the fells by the bainest gate to the Scots king and the Welsh king and all their friends : and she added that she was sorry ; but she doubted nothing of the man's faith, for there was the arrow. Swein drew out the arrow, and gave it to one of his young men, and bade him carry it to Ulfar by the fell-path. The red stranger watched him start, and saw him run up the fell nimbly, and nodded his head : and then Unna signed that he should come to the house for a bite and a sup, and sent the servants back to their haymaking. He ate like a wolf, until little was left for supper ; and stared about him in great wonderment at the house and all that was in it, especially at the three boys, who gaped at him, while they kept hold of their mother's gown. At last he made another of his reverences, and a speech to Swein : walked swiftly through the fields : splashed across the ford : and so vanished into the woods.

Now when the arrow came to Ulfar he was right

glad, and sent it on far and wide, and bade all his neighbours meet at Greenodd. So to Greenodd came two-score men with their war-weapons : and what the giant had left they ate. But it was a point of honour to give to all comers ; and in summer especially there was plenty for the trouble of killing and cooking. They set up tents in the mown field to lodge them, and being all good neighbours there was no rough play to speak of. As for the errand upon which they were come, they held their meeting on the field over against Greenodd across the ford of Crake.

Then began they to ask after the red man their guide, for it was well known by this time that they were bidden to join Constantine the king of Scots and Owain the son of Donal, the new king of Cumberland and Strathclyde, and then to march with all the north upon York by the great highway. But how to come upon that highway none of them knew, nor did they know the paths across the fells for they had kept to themselves by the sea and hardly ventured inland where all was wild forest. As they stood in their assembly, some blaming Swein for putting trust in the red man, and some saying that he ought to have been held by force and not let go, lo and behold the wood opened, and there he was beside them, true to his appointed time.

CHAPTER IX

## THEY TRAVEL THROUGH
## THE FELLS

LITTLE farewell they made, and set out, some on
horseback and some on foot, these two-score men.
The giant striding along led them through wild
woods up hill and down dale.

They stayed that night at the Waterhead of a
long mere, upon a holm beside two rivers that
joined and ran into it. Upon this holm was an
ancient stronghold, built foursquare, and well-nigh
even with the water. The walls were in ruin, and
the roofs of the houses were fallen in. But it
could be seen that this had been a fine burg once
upon a time : for the houses were strongly built of
stone and tiles, and the defences were well planned,
and there were old docks and landing-places
between sharp nabs that ran into the lake. Among
the ruins of the houses were carven pillars and
painted walls, so well done that it was a wonder.
But the place was overgrown with nettles, and the
fairest chambers were choked with briars. A few
of the old houses were patched up, and a handful
of Welsh dwelt in them hugger-mugger. Our
Northmen got fire and a welcome, such as it was :
for it seemed their coming was known, and more
about them than would have been guessed. So

they passed the night in the ruined burg by the waterhead of the winding mere, among the rocky fells and forests.

Next morning their guide took them by a path along the valley until they came to another mere, a little one, under a great nab's scar : over whose axle they climbed about to another lake, not much larger, and with an island in the middle of it, and shores all overgrown with rushes and grass. The mountains around seemed to rise higher and wilder, and on one fell top was seen the likeness of a man crouching down, as if he would roll great rocks upon the road below. They looked at him again and again, but their guide took up a stone and pointed aloft, making signs that the man on the helm of the crag was no living wight, but a man of stone. And yet some of the Northmen were not sorry when they had passed to the other side of his crag, and saw him again in the mist as if he were asleep on his elbow. They were afraid of no mortal man, but they knew that this was a land of wonders and warlocks, and it could be seen that yon stone giant had heard them coming and had stirred in his sleep.

In this mood they climbed over a high hause where the mountains were at their wildest and rough screes fell down from the rocks on either hand through the ragged trees. And soon they had an adventure.

· For on coming down from that pass, they found houses by the path side where it crept along the steep brink. A big man came out to meet

them, swaggering, and dressed in strange ancient
armour of iron bands fitted to his body like an iron
skin. All the same he seemed very filthy, and
sodden with drink. He gave them to wit in
Welsh that he was governor of this borderland for
the Cumbrian king, and seemingly a greater man
than the king himself. " For," said he, " Owain
and his father are no Romans, like the other King
Donal that went before them. But I," said he,
" am of right Roman blood and my name is
Elphin map Rhydderch map Caradoc : and I let no
man nor woman pass without tribute."

" Ah ! " said Swein, " here we have one of the
folk who made this gate. I guessed they were of
the troll's kin. Look you, friends, no iron will
bite upon him."

And since the fellow would not let them pass,
Swein with little ado smote out his fist, as it might
be to try what would happen : and the brainpan of
Elphin was cracked against his own stone door
post. Their guide gazed awhile upon him, and
turned him over with his foot, saying nought but
" Aigh ! " And so they passed on.

Then the road took them on the edge of wonderful great cliffs by the brink of a long mere, in the
middle of which was a narrow place, and a wath.
Here there were houses, poor enough, of men who
seemed to be the giant's kin, and there our travellers
stayed for the night. Next morning they crossed
the wath, and at the foot of the lake they came to a
place where four dales met among high mountains
and crags. And here there was a sweet spot alone

in the wilderness, with meadowland and a little brook coming down from Helvellyn through the leas, to meet the great river that ran from the lake, and turning sharply round went by a deep valley. They took notice of this dale because of its sweetness in the midst of wild rocks and forests, and because it is not often one sees four dales meeting in one spot like the rays of the sign of Thor.

But their path led them onward through the deep valley of the Greta, with crags on one hand and a roaring river or spreading swamps on the other, until they came to a wide plain, and on the other side of it, at the foot of the mountain Blencathra, their path struck eastward. By nightfall they came to another of those ancient ramparted villages of the Welsh: and hard by, across a little dell, the army lay at Penruddock.

Owain the king received them well, and thanked them for their coming, and promised them the foremost place when they should meet the Saxons. In his tent they met Ketel Bolster as Swein had called him, and the Northmen from the Solway, and they fell in talk together. But before they had spoken many words, men came running in through the lanes of tents, crying out " They are here ! " Owain bade them have peace : and took Swein and his chief men, and went out to the brow of the hill. There in the twilight they saw the valley beyond thronged with a great multitude, and knew, by the lights that started up from point to point, that Athelstan with all his power was camping in the fields of Dacre.

## CHAPTER X

## DACRE CROSS

DACRE was then, as it is now, the name of a pleasant vale, on the border between the plain country of Cumberland and the mountains of Lakeland. Among the mountains at that time were dwelling only wild Welsh, but in the plain country were many homesteads of Anglians, dotted here and there beside the old high-road.

These Anglians were Christian people, and had priests and monks among them. One of their abbeys was at Dacre; an abbey famous for the last two hundred years and more. The Welsh of Penrith and Penruddock and Blencow lived thus alongside of the Anglians: not always quiet neighbours perhaps, but yet on some terms of neighbourhood; and if not good subjects to Owain king of Cumbria, still reckoned within his borders.

So when Athelstan had news about the plots of Owain and Constantine to put back Sigtrygg's sons on their father's throne, he marched from York by the old high-road straight over the hills; and in three days he was here at Dacre guesting with the monks. And his foes, who had come south too late to carry the war into the country of York, found nothing left for them to do but to agree with him as best they might.

Athelstan the king sat in Dacre church, and the kings of the north swore to him as they had sworn to his father Eadward ; and they gave their hostages into his hands, and renounced their dealings with the idolaters, namely those heathen Danes, the sons of Sigtrygg. "For," said Athelstan, "it is a shame if we, being Christian men and ruling Christian men, suffer these unbaptized pagans to ravage a Christian land, to burn the churches, and slay the monks, and rob the holy women our sisters. And if we three but stand together, we might clear the whole island of such knaves, and keep it clear for ourselves and our people, in peace and plenty."

To such talk as that while Owain and Constantine were well agreed, and all the readier because Athelstan's host was bigger than both of theirs.

Now Constantine had with him a young son of his, yet unchristened ; and Athelstan, willing to knit himself closer to his new friends, said that he would stand godfather to the child ; for in those days it was thought nearer than kinship by blood to be god-sib, or bound by holy water and the vows of baptism. So they brought the young child to the church, and baptized him, and Athelstan stood his godfather.

When he was out of the water, and dressed in white, with white linen wrapped about his head, said the priest, "Here is water, king, as the Scripture says : what should hinder these from being baptized ?" and he pointed to the Northmen who were standing without, and neither signed them-

E

selves with the cross nor bent the knee at prayer, but stared in through the church porch at the gilded imagery, and at the glass windows that Bishop Wilfrith had put there in ancient times.

With that there was some shrinking back among those who had been most eager to look on; and Athelstan turned and fixed his gaze upon Swein, and spoke in the Northmen's tongue, for he knew it well.

"What sayest thou, friend? Wilt thou set the good example?"

"King," answered he, "I am a primesigned man and no church robber."

(For it must be known that many of the heathen were, as one may say, half-baptized; not that they meant to change their faith, but in order to have dealings in trade and otherwise with Christians, who might have no communion with the unbelievers).

"And," added Swein, "I have a mind to stay as I am."

"But if I bid thee?" said the young king.

"Eadward thy father asked no such thing of me, when I took him for father and lord two years ago."

"Why, brother, I seem to have some inkling of thy face. Wast not thou the brawler of Bakewell?"

With that they laughed and Swein reddened, and replied somewhat angrily, "Saving a king's presence, I was no brawler, nor did thy father call me so, to my face."

"Nor behind thy back, believe me, good man. For I tell truth when I say that after all were gone, and we were together at supper, my father said this to me : Boy, he said, we have done a good day's work ; and I remember well how he cracked a great nut when he said it. But, said he, the best touch of my kingcraft, for many a year, has been the winning of that stout franklin and his fellows. And he charged me to leave no stone unturned to get the love of you Northmen, such as had settled peaceably within our borders, and were busied in tilling lands hitherto waste, and in carrying trade about our coasts. Now, what shall I give thee, since thou dost refuse the best of gifts in my keeping ? "

"King," said Swein, " they say we Northmen are greedy of gold, and of blood, and of plunder alone. But by this I know that thou art wiser than other men, and bearest a grey head on those young shoulders. Truth it is when thou sayest that we are busied in tilling waste places, and in sea-trading ; and this no man can gainsay. And, indeed, if at times we are ready to fight, and to fight our best, it is but to keep the homes we have made with our own hands, and to give them over no less than we hold them into the safe keeping of our little ones."

Then Athelstan thought awhile and said : " It has been in my mind now these many days that it would be a wise law, if every such brave seafaring merchant who has made three voyages with his own goods in his own ship, should be called Thane of England. Will that cap fit, friend?"

"Well, king," answered Swein, "many a voyage have I made with my own bulk in my own ship, cheaping a little and——"

"And taking what came in thy way?" broke in the king with a smile.

"That's as you may call it," said Swein.

"Well, for the law the Witan must look to it; and for thee, friend, come to me once again when thy mind is made up, after talk with the priest here, and with the good monks hard by."

The priest was glad enough to talk with Swein, and so were the monks, for that matter; and they went near to tearing him in pieces between them.

First he must away to see the monastery; and in it was a carved shrine of gold and enamel, curiously worked, and holding their treasure. Swein looked for a crown of jewels at the least; but lo and behold, it was only a lock of hair. But they said that this lock of hair was from the head of Cuthbert the great saint of their faith; and that it had been cut from his dead body when his grave was opened after eleven years and relics were found whole and uncorrupted. And then they told Swein of the wonderful things which that lock of hair could do; how it had healed a young man who was diseased in his eyes, and such like, as was written in the book of venerable Beda. Swein wondered at the casket, but he took little heed of the relic, saying he thanked them, and he would come back to them when his eyes ached, if no wise wife at home could cure him.

Then they carried him out to the kirkgarth, where was standing a great pillar of sandstone round below, foursquare in the waist, and at the top the head of a cross. It was covered with patterns on two sides, and on two with leaves in whose tendrils, most delicately wrought, birds and beasts were climbing about.

" See ! " said the monk, " the four gospellers ; or rather, the four creatures that signify them."

" I know," said Swein. " Have I never seen them in Ireland ?—but never so well shaped. That lion with the wings, he is Mark. And there is the snake that means the enemy. And the cross at the top I know well, but you have no man hanging upon it. Christ, your Lord you call him—Odin, I say as I was taught—should be hanging in the tree, as the rhyme says :

> I wavered, I wot,
> On the windy tree
> Nine whole nights :
> With weapon wounded,
> Offered to Odin,
> Myself to myself.
>
> Gazing groundward
> The runes I gathered ;
> Weeping I wooed them,
> And won me down."

" Ah ! " cried the monk eagerly, " thou are not far from the kingdom of God. For what saith the Scripture! As in Adam all died, even so in Christ shall all be made alive. Come with me, and the Lord open thine eyes."

Then he took Swein into the little church, and the sunshine came through the windows upon the altar and on the crucifix standing there.

"Behold," said the monk kneeling, "one hanging on the tree, wounded with the spear, very God of very God: given by himself to himself, that we who are his body might know the truth, and that the truth might make us free."

And more he added, earnestly entreating his guest: until Swein laid his hand on the frail shoulder of the monk and said gravely:

"Young man, these two-score years I have followed the gods of my fathers: and one while they have been good to me, and another while they have been evil-minded. Now I will not lightly take a new god at the bidding of yonder king; nay, not to be Thane or Earl. Nor do I wholly understand all thy words, though I reckon they are good words, and spoken from a good heart. But this I say, that no priest nor church shall ever be the worse for me or mine; and when my day of need comes, if thy God will help me, he shall be my God."

He took the monk's hand, and went his way. But the monk knelt there, weeping passionately and praying, "Oh God, give me that man's soul. Nay, not unto me, oh Lord, but unto Thy name be the glory."

# CHAPTER XI

## THE GIANT'S BOON

HAYMAKING was begun when our Northmen started on their journey to Dacre; and it was not finished when they came back, as empty-handed as they went. When they were once again in the hall at home, and the red man had brought them safe and sound through flood and fell, Swein said to his wife, "Now that this man our guide has taken us in good faith through strange places, and brought us home again, though little we have got by our travelling unless it be gain to be no worse off than we were, but the more assured of peace and quietness; I would not send him away without thanks, but I would give him a gift, even if it be a good weapon, or as many sheep as he can drive. Ask him then to make his choice, and he shall not find us stingy."

Unna agreed very readily to this; and when she had set it forth, the red man was silent for a time, looking round as if to choose something out of the house. At last he stood up, and made a long speech in his own tongue, waving his arms and shaking his head. While he spoke, they saw her grow pale as grass, and the tears came into her eyes.

" Swein," she said, " and friends all, here is a
hard thing for us to answer; and indeed I know
not myself what to do. For the man says that he
has enough and to spare of all the goods he needs ;
and that he is a chief among his own people, so
that he may not take a hired man's wages for
service done rather to his king than to strangers.
But if I understand him aright he says that he saw
at Dacre how men had respect to thee, Swein
Biornson; and that even the great king of the
Saxons spoke with thee friendly, as with a great
chief. And, moreover, I gather from his words
that he has some foresight from his own dreams
or from a wise man's, that you strangers are to
be mighty in this land, and that nothing will stand
against you in the end; and that you will wipe
his people from the face of the earth, and take from
them the homes of their fathers. Now he says
that he would be thy friend and brother; and for
a pledge of our peace, he would have nothing else
but the fostering of one of our sons."

With that they all cried out astonished, and
Swein laughing a little and harshly, said, " Tell him
that we do not give our lads to giants and wild
men of the woods nowadays, even if Signy gave
her child to Sigmund once on a time, as the old
song says."

" Nay," she said, " I will not anger him, or he
will do us a bad turn one of these days."

" Tell him that we humbly thank his lordship
for the honour, and one day we will wait on his
lordship at his lordship's palace,"

But the red man, though he could make nothing of the words, knew very well from the horse-laugh and the rough gesture of Swein that he was despised and his offer scorned; and before Unna could speak, he dashed his great club on the ground so that it tore a hole in the paving, and made the cobbles fly. Then turning round, he went swiftly and disappeared into the woods as before.

They looked at one another as if mischief should come next, but Swein said, " Take courage, wife, and never fear that I will give up child of ours to such a foster-father; and you, friends all, be on your guard, and keep a watch on the ford and the woods, so that we be not taken unawares. As for you, barns, let me not say it twice : stay with your mother, and never wander away out of her sight, or the sight of the good fellows who have charge of you."

Days passed, and months ; and all that winter nothing was seen or heard of the red man ; until it became a jest among them. For when any of the boys were unruly, they would say to snape him, " Folk would think the giant had thy fostering."

But what with fear of this wood-man, and what with lack of neighbours, Orm and Hundi and Thorstein grew up in their father's house, and were not put out to foster-parents like many children of that day. For all that, they were not brought up in idleness, to be spoiled lads and good for nought ; since, although there was plenty of servants, it was the way of these people to do their own work, and to show their mastery in craft of hand as well as in cunning of head.

There was a smithy on the farm; for how else could they shoe their nags or fettle their weapons? And Swein was proud to be called master smith of them all, and would spend many a winter day at the anvil, forging the iron they brought in their boats from Plain Furness. So the boys picked up something of the craft, maybe not so workmanlike as others, and yet serviceably for the needs of people whose things were less for show than for use. Their fine jewellery and goldsmith's work they had from abroad; but even so there was always some conceit of daintiness or quaintness in the way they turned out their homely jobs, because their time was before them, and they liked smithying, and lingered over it as a pastime; curling the horns of a door-latch or a candle-stick into ringlets with the tongs; twisting the bar of a horse-bit into a screw, and engraving a blade with devices or punching it into patterns. And every bit of work was a lesson to the boys.

Beside smithying there was always woodwork to be done, for their houses were wooden, and many things for which we use potter's wares, they made of wood; as cups and platters and all sorts of vessels. In the winter evenings especially this work went on round the hearth, while the women spun and wove. The lads were not long at whittling sticks before they were set to make arrows and shafts for weapons and tools, and it was a proud day when they made their first piggin

with hoops and staves complete. And from that
they got to carving, since these people were as
nice about their woodwork as their iron, and could
not abide a blank kist-panel or door-post, after
they had once got roof raised and land stubbed.

Moreover, on these winter evenings there was
story-telling and singing of ballads, which let the
lads into some knowledge of olden times, of the
kings and the gods, and especially adventures in
strange lands. Add to this that their mother, half
Irish as she was, and the Welsh thralls with whom
they consorted, as children will with servants,
taught them something of other tongues than their
own. And Unna showed them their letters,
drawing the runestaves with a charred stick on a
board for them to carve. As to book-learning,
they got on very well without it.

## CHAPTER XII

### RAIDS

SPRINGTIME was now come and the children of
Greenodd went with their playmates from the
thralls' cottages to roam the woods. For then were
the hollows among the knolls by Crake side all
carpeted with golden lilies and dim white wind-
flowers. And when the time of these was over,
bluebells, sweet scented, and growing as thick as
grass, covered the glades. Thorstein, who was
now four years old, and some of his playfairs were
in the woods one day; and their game was to
make a queen of the prettiest girl, dressing a bower
for her and crowning her with bluebells. In the
midst of it who should come suddenly upon them
but a wild red man, bellowing, they said, like a
bull, and shaking his great club as if he meant to
kill them all. But he only caught the biggest and
best looking of the boys, and dragged him off.
When the boy bealed and screamed, the robber
nipped him round the throat, and soon stopped
his noise. The children ran home with their knees
trembling, and said that a giant had got their playfellow to eat him. But whatever he did with him
he did not eat him; for next morning before the
men could start to lait the lad, he came down the
beck with his head broken.

Said Swein, " No use to shut the door when the roof has fallen in." Then he sent a good gift to the thrall whose child was lost, telling him to wipe his eyes with it ; and forbade the youngsters wandering in woods or out of sight. So all was quiet for a time, and if there were uneasiness about robbers, it was no more than what everyone felt everywhere in those days, when by sea and shore men carried their lives in their hands, and trusted to luck to keep their women and children from bloodshed and slavery.

In the next winter there was much snow, and the distant mountains were curd-white, both at Yule and for many a week after. Even the moor-lands were covered and the forests were choked ; and when great storms blew, the mealy snow would drift in streaming clouds, and fill all the hollow places and the gills ; so that many wild beasts were buried in the drifts, and many came down into the valleys, where the snow lay not so thick and melted away between whiles. Sheep and cattle needed double care ; for though most of the stock was killed and hung in smoke, some beasts always had to be kept, and fed with the hay of the summer, and holly boughs, which the shepherds cut and let them pick up when they took them out from the byres and folds. Even so there was always danger of drifts, and the burying of whole flocks in the snow ; and then they had to dig them out, which was a great labour to the men, but a fine playtime for Thorstein and his brothers. For to the boys the snow was like fairyland, and rare enough to be something of a marvel to children in sheltered Greenodd by the sea. What storms they feel there come mostly from the warm south-west, and if the wind blows from north-east it brings sunshine, with blue sky and black frost that vanishes away long before noon.

One day Thorstein went with the shepherds and their lads to an uplying fold to serve the sheep, and found the snow much trampled, as though wild beasts has been there, for all there was a high turf dyke around it, with a sharp fence on the top such as no wolves were like to climb. So the shepherd began counting out the flock, in their way which Thorstein learnt from him: " Un, dau, tri, y-pedwar, y-pump: chwech, y-saith, y-wyth, naw, deg." And we may say that our old folk still use this way of reckoning little changed but to make the words easier with rhyme, as: " Yan, tyan, teddera, meddera, pimp; haata, slaata, sour, down, dick——" and so forth.

When he had counted a score he marked it off on his fingers, or scored a notch on a stick, and began again. And so counting he found that two sheep were gone; and worse than that, they saw, by the blood on the snow and by the footprints, that thieves had cut their throats and carried them off. So away they went to track the thieves at once, which was easy enough because of the snow. Before long, stopping to listen, they heard a crackling of branches ahead, and shouted, and put Thorstein in the rear, and pressed forward. Then were seen through the leafless trees three men, or not men but giants they seemed, long and gaunt and red-haired. One had a sheep on his shoulders, and another had a sheep on his shoulders, not a little encumbered as they pushed their ways through the underwood and thick tangle.

The shepherds had gone too far to go back; and beside that, they were armed, while the thieves had only their cudgels. But when it came to blows, such was the tangle in the wood that they were soon scattered; one was stuck in a thicket, and another floored with a broken head, and a third with a broken arm; and the robbers were off and away. So when they came to collect their forces there was one wanting, a shepherd's son. They shouted and searched the wood as well as they might, for it was beginning to grow dark. In the end they were forced to return home without him, and their sheep were gone and all.

When they brought Thorstein to the house and told their tale, Swein listened with a very long face, and saw to their hurts; for it was the chief's business to be surgeon, both to handle wounds until the blood stopped, and to set broken limbs and bind them. It was the lady's to make drinks of herbs for medicine. Some good drink Unna gave them, and they went home; but Swein and she talked late that night after Thorstein was asleep.

The next day Swein himself, with a band of men well armed, set off early, and soon found the place where the fight had been. Thenceforward by the broken branches, for it had snowed and the tracks were covered, they followed the robbers up the fell and towards the moors. But when they came out of the wood upon the heather, what should they see but the boy who had been carried off, lying on the ground, and dead. It was plain that the robbers had knocked him on the head; though why they should take him all that way, and wherefore they should kill him at the last, nobody could tell. Swein gave a good gift to the shepherd whose son had been killed, saying that he could get no other atonement at the time; but that one day he would gather his neighbours together and clear the fells of such vermin. And he said no more of the matter, unless it were of nights to the mistress.

# CHAPTER XIII

## *UNNA'S COUNSEL*

ALL that year King Constantine and King Owain were quiet, and held to the peace of Dacre. But King Guthferth Ivarson of Dublin, to whom Olaf Cuaran had fled, was not in the treaty, and thought himself in no way bound to refrain from attacking the realms of Britain, but quite otherwise.

So King Guthferth and his nephew Olaf Cuaran and their host crossed the sea, and landed, as our story has it, at Ellenburg by the mouth of the river Ellen in Cumberland, where now stands Maryport, and before those times stood some old Roman city. Thence there was the good road that the Romans had made, straight to Carlisle, and so to Penrith, and over Stainmoor. In a week or so they were again in York; but not for long. For as soon as King Athelstan heard of it he went northward, and drove them home by the way they came. There was a deal of confused fighting, of which folk never will know, and maybe never did know, the rights. And sorely he blamed Owain for giving the Danes passage through his kingdom. But Owain came off this time with the excuse that in Strathclyde he had enough on his hands, and could not be answerable for vikings who forced their way through the extremest borders of his dominion. Yet when the same thing happened again and again and every time the viking host left behind it stragglers and settlers to hold strong places and good lands on the Cumberland coasts, as a flood tide leaves its wreckage on the shore, then the English king was forced to take stronger measures with the Cumbrians, as the tale tells in the end.

Meanwhile Athelstan held counsel about that borderland where our Northmen lived. Neither Swein nor any of his neighbours had come in to him, ready to be baptized and to take his service; or maybe he might have set one of them over these parts as Thane or Earl, to rule the country in his name. On the other hand, the land of Cartmel was already in the holding of the priests, and they no doubt were instant in their claims to take under them the whole of which they held a part. So Athelstan, for the good of his soul, and for the souls of the Northmen who should be brought into the fold, and for the better ruling of these outlying borders, gave to the priests of York Minster all Amounderness—that is, the land from the Ribble to the great bight we now call More-cambe Bay.

After a while came the summoner from York to take tithe and tax from the Northmen, as he was wont to do from the Cartmel people. But they made short work of him, and when next there was a meeting, loud talk was held about the matter. Even Swein Biornson, though he had loved Athelstan when he saw him at Dacre, was angry with him now, for giving away what was not his own to give, and lands that he never had so much as set eyes on.

Then stood up one and said, " News, friends ! I have been lately seafaring by way of the South-isles and thereabouts ; and wherever I came the talk was that Olaf Cuaran had gone over from Dublin to Scotland, and that Constantine the king had received him as guest ; and more than that, had given him his daughter to wife. Now, what think you of that, friends ? "

There was a great hubbub when this came out, for not a man of them but knew what it meant, and they were glad to think that if they themselves had a quarrel with Athelstan, friends would be easy to find. For by giving his daughter to Olaf the viking, Constantine had already broken the peace of Dacre.

Well, some were for war, and some for waiting ; and they talked it over this way and that, until Swein bade them have peace. " For," said he " I know this Athelstan, that he is a brisk man and full of good counsel ; and I know the Saxons that they are not to be despised. If we alone set ourselves up to make war we shall be fools ; for they have men enough to sweep us off the face of the earth, as a thrall sweeps out a byre with a besom. But if Constantine and Owain and our kinsmen in the north are agreed, and come together to invade the south country, well and good. My rede is to lie still and watch the weather."

Now Mistress Unna was all this while in the

house, cooking the supper for Swein and the men of the Thing, and little did she know that all the men of Furness and Amounderness were being ruled by her counsels.

Lucky it was for our Northmen that they took Unna's counsel, and listened to Swein when he told them of the briskness of Athelstan. For Constantine, who had received Olaf Cuaran and given him his daughter, before ever he could draw his host together to invade England, while he was yet preparing for war, saw the ships of Athelstan bear down upon his coast ; and fleeing inland, whom should he meet but Athelstan himself with an army, come through Northumberland to avenge the peace of Dacre. And great mischief was done before the English went home with pledges of a new peace wrung from the Scots, who for their part had no mind to keep it, any more than their oaths of seven years ago, and only waited for the day when they might take their revenge.

But if the York priests complained of their new liege-men, and told Athelstan on his way home how their summoner had been treated ; and if Athelstan laughed and bade them study to be quiet, as the epistle says, and mind their own business ; it is no more than was likely. For he had enough to do without taking his host across the Keel to gather tithes from the Northmen of Amounderness.

## CHAPTER XIV

## THE FINDING OF
## THURSTON WATER

Now the story leaves those great kings and their wars, to tell of Thorstein Sweinson, and how he went up the river Crake, and how he found the great water at the river-head; the same that in old times was called Thorstane's water, and we call Coniston lake, from the name of our village hard by it.

In the year after the ravaging of Scotland, Thorstein was eleven winters old, and a great lad; sturdy at all games of strength, and skilful enough in all kinds of work that a lad was set to do. He could catch a nag on the fell, and ride it home through the heather; make an arrow, and shoot it to the mark; handle the smith's tools or the woodwright's; swim, and row, wrestle and race with his brothers, and often beat them, and always beat the thralls' boys. Most of all he took pleasure in going about with the herds, to look after the beasts and the sheep on the summer-hills; and when they were once out and away, he would egg them on to take him farther, to see the little dells and winding valleys on either side of the Crake, as if he might find there something of the great world which he had heard about and longed to wander through.

It was nigh upon seven years since the wild men of the fells had made their last raid and carried off the thrall's son; but still Swein would often warn his boys to keep within sight of home, and bid them stay by their mother if he himself were abroad. But he might as well have warned the smoke not to go out of the chimney. For northern blood stirred in the lads; and Thorstein often looked down the firth to seaward, and wished he were big enough to go viking in a ship of his own. Orm said he would go with him if it were trading he meant; and thought that they might make a deal of money by selling the thralls' children. Upon which Thorstein hit him in the face, and said, "Thou shan't get our little May-queen for one." And he spoke no more of his plans to Orm.

Hundi was a better friend to Thorstein, and they talked a deal together of the travels they should take and the deeds they should do. There were those great mountains in the far distance, always beckoning to them; peopled with giants and fairies —had not their father often told them of the stone man that kept the road beyond Grasmere? and had they not the dim remembrance, not easily let die, of the red giant? They knew by hearsay of wide lakes among the fells, lying all alone for the first adventurer to take and hold. The beck that flowed through their fields, and the greater Leven that they could see from the howe or from Leg-barrow winding far away among the hills, came down, so the Welshmen said, out of wide waters full of fish and haunted by fowl in countless flocks. And as they sat on the rocks at Crakemouth when the tide was low moulding clay arrowheads in the rune-shaped clifts and chinks of the smooth rock, they wondered what troll or fairy had been there with chisel and mallet, and what more marvellous marvel there might be to find in the unknown wilds beyond.   Crake, the rocky river, came down night and day, sometimes fierce and swollen, sometimes faint and shrunken, but always singing over its rocks the same song of enticement.   " If we could only track the beck," they said, " and find the great water, and take the fish and fowl, and build a house by the shore and make a boat ! "

So at last the wish grew into a plan, and the plan into a purpose.   When nobody was looking they were to slip away, follow the Crake to its mere, take the land about it, and make a backwood bigging of their own.   They filled a bag with meal, took their knives in their belts, and set off one morning early, as though they were going for a day with the shepherds.   But where the fields ended, they took the path to the outlying folds ; and when they were near the folds, they turned through the woods to the river, so that they might not be seen, and scrambled for a great way up the stony channel.   It was only half filled, because, as often happens in those parts, the spring had been dry, and the rainy weather was yet to come on, after the days began to shorten.

For a while it was easy work ; there is a flat

shore on the left hand, and they could run over the shingle even where the water went swiftly and fell in eddies and foam over rock-ridges. But soon the hills on either side close in; the banks are steep; the river foams beneath thick trees which spread their branches, making the squirrel's bridge overhead. Thus it is even nowadays, but in yon old times in many places great firs had fallen right across the deep channel, or huge oaks had lost their hold of the rocky bank from very weight of age, and had rolled into the torrent, to be weirs and dams that held the water and flooded the banks; so that what with the swamp, wherever there was a bit of flat shore, and what with the rock walls, or the slippery sodden tufts of moss and fern, wherever the gill-banks were brant, the lads made but little way. And whoever has stood upon Spark Brig and looked up-bank and down-bank, and dreamt over a time when all the mills and houses were unbuilt, and the land uncleared, and nothing but wild timber, dank and dense, filled the dale, with the logs that rotted where they fell, and the brambles and creepers that matted the growing trunks together; and wild bulls and wild boars, wolves and cats, hag-worms and lizards, and maybe a bear or two, tenanted the place: he will know what the adventure of those two boys was like. And whoever has fought his way up one of our moorland gills where the land is still rough, will know how they stumbled over the shallows, and scrambled over the boulders, and waded the mires, and swam the dubs, as they came through the jaws of Crake, and out into the easier ground by the eyot beneath Lowick Green, as it is now. There, if the river was less rough, the trees were still thick and the banks steep ; and on the right hand the fells seemed to come nearer ; and standing out through the black fir-trees high overhead, grey brows of crag seemed to frown and nod above them, as they sat on a great stone in mid-stream to take their breath.

The king-fishers flitted past, blue flashes in the green gloom. Where a ray of sunshine came in through the vault of trees overhead and pierced the brown water, they could see, beneath mossy rocks fringed with fern, little dippers running over the bottom among the trout, and as free as if they were on dry land, for all the rushing of the water. Now and again a wild animal ran down to drink, and started back crashing into the wood ; but there was no sign of houses, nor of men dwelling in this uncouth wilderness.

They toiled on again, mounting the stream where it breaks over long-drawn ledges, around a rocky eyot at a sharp bend, and through a swampy tarn (as it was then) till they came to the spot where Lowick bridge now stands. It was high noon. They sat down on the steep bank above the swamp ; and taking handfuls of the meal from their bag, soaked it with the clear fresh water and made their dinner. When it was done, said Hundi, " Well, old forge-ahead, how much farther ? For my part I call the shepherds' tales all Welsh lies. There is no great water that we can see, only this dirty puddle ; and we shall have work enough to get home before supper-time, down the screes we have climbed and this waste of rubbish."

" Nay," said Thorstein, " the beck must come from somewhere, and I mean to see the end of it."

" What, and sleep in a tree like a squirrel ? "

" Why not, if I must, thou slug-a-bed ? The nights are short and warm enough."

" Well, then," said Hundi, " I will sit on the howe over there, and wait until the conquering hero comes back.   I'll count a hundred, and then."

" And then go home like a wise lad to thy mother, and say Thorstein is coming to-morrow with news, and a great fish out of Thorstein's mere ; for it will be none of Hundi's."

" Hundi's howe is here, Thorstein's mere is nowhere."   And indeed afterwards the story says that Hundi lived hard by, and was in the end buried on that howe ; but that is still to tell.   Said he, " A wilful beast must gang his own gate, and I'll not mar sport, nor splash thy mere to frighten thy whales.   Come, Thorstein, don't be a fool. Turn back with me now, or rue it ! "

" Neither, dear lad ; and don't anger me, but hie thy ways home, and bid them not worry. Happen I'll light on my journey's end sooner than we think for."

" Happen thou'll light on mischief sooner than thou think'st for.   Come along, I say."

" Go along, I say.   We can't miss the road, for its down-bank for thee and up-bank for me to the end."

" Nay, that's an ill speech," said Hundi, " for parting."

" Well, then, home for thee, and away in the wide world for me, for evermore. Will that suit ? "

" Nor that either. I wish thee luck, and thy big fish ; and I'll foreset the scolding that awaits thee ; and have thy breakfast kept warm ; for yon bag of meal will be gone before to-morrow, if I know aught."

" Good lad, then ; we part friends ; " and Hundi turned and slid down the bank and splashed down stream ; for he was always an easy-going lad.

But Thorstein toiled on as before, and found his work no less at first ; for he had to win his way up Lowick force and through the swamps at its head. But then he saw, at last, rising above the trees, a crest and a cone of high rugged fells, distant indeed, but not a mere blue line as he had seen them from the heights of Greenodd. The afternoon sun threw its lights and shadows on the great scars of Dowcrags, and the rocks of the Coniston Old Man stood out bold in the blue air.

The lad's heart leapt up, and he shouted as he plunged again in the rapids that swirled beneath the wild steeps on his right, and the long, dark slopes of Blawith, the Black-wood, on the other hand. By and by he was lost again in the crooked ravine where the Nibthwaite Mills now stand, where the water narrowed to half its former breadth, and slid over ranks of rock, sloping downwards like carven tables, or a giant's stairway, sunken and aslew. But at the head of every force, there were the great fells again in sight, and every time nearer and clearer, grander and more wonderful. At last he came to a sweet round tarn. It was bedded in the woods, and the likeness of every several branch lay upon the water. Thorstein shouted : but then he stayed. Was this the mere he had come so far to seek ? and no more than this ?

He pressed forward, round the miry edges of the tarn, and stumbled through the narrows of Arklid. Hitherto the stream had been ever narrower, and, but for a few ledges and flats, ever steeper ; but here it suddenly became both still and deep, and opened out into breadth. Thorstein's heart beat hard when the wood thinned, and the waterway broadened, and the world grew brighter, and lo, beyond, a great gleam of blue, and a blaze of golden sky.

Close beside him, seal-bushes fringed the shilloe beds, bulrushes stood in their ranks right out into the shallows, and purple flags and white and yellow water-lilies lay along the edges of the lake. On either hand, seaming the deep forest that clothed the sides of the valley, sharp craggy spurs came down, as it were gateposts to the hall of hills ; and broke at their bases into long nabs, rounded here and rocky there, running far out into the mere and tufted to the water-edge with dark oaks and dark firs. And between, there were blue nooks of ripple reflecting the evening sky, and the

wild ducks and teal swam through the ripple, and
the gulls floated above it; and in round spots a
hundred rings showed how the fish were rising.

Thorstein climbed a howe on the left; and as
he climbed, the lake opened up before him. Beyond the nearer woods there was the deep of blue,
and the lonely island in the midst of it; and from
his feet, away into the uttermost distance, the huge
fells, tossing like the breakers on a stormy beach,
and rolling away and afar like the heaving waves
of the sea. And over them late sunset brooded in
the north, with bars of level cloud, purple and dun,
and fading rose-flecks overhead.

Unwearied in his exultation, the lad ran down
to the shore again, and stripping off hood and
kirtle, hose and shoes, all stained and ragged with
scrambling through brake and briar, he waded out
into deep water, plunged beneath, and swam
sturdily through the calmness. Then he flagged at
last, and crept ashore, and donned his clothes, and
looked about him for a safe night-lair; smiling as
he thought of Hundi's horror at sleeping like a
squirrel. He crept into the boughs of a great
spreading oak, and its thick leaves sheltered him
like a thatched roof and hid him like the hangings
of a shut-bed. The level clouds drew together;
the purple colour darkened into black; and a line
of dusky light alone lingered in the north over
Helvellyn, while he slept, dreamless.

## CHAPTER XV

### *THE GIANT GETS*
### *HIS FOSTERLING*

THORSTEIN slept on in the tree long after the day
had dawned through those level clouds; for at
midsummer in Lakeland it is never black night;
the sun only dives, as it were, behind a fell or two,
and up again; and you can follow its track by the
light that travels round the north, like the ripples
which betray a diver in shoal water. But this
dawning was a dull one, for those level clouds had
lowered, and thickened, and turned to rain; and
wind came up from the seaward, as the gulls had
foretold. And yet it mattered little to the lad in
his oak-tree lair, except that no loud singing of
birds awoke him, and the dimness of the light let
him sleep on when he should have been well on
his way homeward. For as to the plan of taking
land and building a house and a boat, that was out
of his mind now that Hundi was gone. To take
land, one must go round it with fire, and have
witnesses to the deed. Some other day he would
come back, now that he knew the road. And it
was lonely waking there in the damp, hungry and
stiff, with all that waste of wilderness to tread
before ever he saw home again.

Back along the bank of Crake and round the

little tarn went Thorstein until he heard, in the woods on his right hand, shouting, and the voices of men. At once his heart came into his mouth and he stood stock-still to listen. Could it be Hundi come back, and the Greenodd folk in search of him? What if they should go forward and find his mere, and he away and out of it all? What of the chance of a good bag of meal or a barley cake somewhere about them? For he was both clemmed and starved. So he crept through the wood, and now and again the noise came louder. He followed it, slowly forcing his way among the deep fern and the brambles under the great trees; the voices were heard more plainly now, singing and shouting in a strange manner. It was not Hundi and the Greenodd folk; but who? Thorstein was drawn by a great desire to know this secret of the woods, and to add one more marvel to the story he should tell at supper.

On the top of a little howe, clear of trees, but rocky and ferny like the wildest moorland, there was a great heap of stones, whether grave or cot it would be hard to tell; and beside it in the fern sat huge men, red haired and red-bearded, crane-legged and clumsy handed and jolter-headed, clothed rudely in skins, and devouring great ugly gobbets of flesh from a roebuck they had killed, and seemed to eat with little or no cooking. Thorstein gazed at them open-mouthed and astonished; it was like a dream of the wonders he had pictured to himself, but never fully hoped to set eyes on.

The branch he held by, snapped; and forthwith there was a terrible shout, and a crash on his head, and he seemed as in a dream to be falling down a dark pit.

Then it was all light, grey light, and no green gloom of the woods; and beneath him the new fern-fronds fled away, as he was carried by someone or something swiftly over the wide moor. He began to know that he was weary and in a great pain of his head; and at every stride of his bearer he was jerked so that it hurt him. He kicked and struggled; the huge red man put him into the middle of a deep heather-tuft, and set himself down to look at the lad, as a cat watches a mouse.

Then Thorstein rose on his knees and tried to scramble away, but the giant man just reached out and gave him a great batt with his hand, that sent him heels over head, scratching his face in the heather. Then the same thing happened again; and the third time Thorstein plucked himself together and flew at the giant, snatching out his knife, and minded in his rage to stick it in anywhere or anyhow. But the giant never moved off the stone where he sat; he just caught the knife in one hand, and with the other crushed the lad down. He looked at the knife long and curiously, then he nodded and laughed to himself. Then he looked at Thorstein where he lay on his back, kicking up the tufts of moss; and then he waved the knife as if to draw it over Thorstein's throat. Thorstein shut his eyes and his mouth as tightly as he could.

The cold knife cut his neck a little, and the blood came; Thorstein waited to be killed. The rain pattered on his eyelids, and when he opened them again half blinded, but not with tears, the giant was looking at the knife-handle and the pattern on its blade; and nodding to himself. Then he picked up the lad under one arm, and strode off through the heather.

## CHAPTER XVI

## THE FELL-FOLK'S HOME

BEYOND the heather was the giant's home, on the fell between Blawith and Broughton. You may find the spot even nowadays with little searching, if you make for a farm called Heathwaite, and up behind it to the brackenbeds between Kirkby Moor and Blawith Knott. There among the borrans which the mowers have heaped of autumns to clear the land for their leys, there is a deal of other borrans, and older ones, that no man minds the building of; though yearly work on the land keeps them up, so to say. You can see that they are ruins of a kind of homestead, with its little garths, and greater intakes on a ridge of fell. On one hand there are the waste wet mosses of the moor, and on the other hand, far below, the great flats of Woodlands, dotted with old farmsteads and thwaites, and surrounded by the tossing rocky range of Dunnerdale fells, from the Coniston Old Man on the right hand away down to Black Comb and the glittering sea.

In a high place like this, people might live for many a long year unseen and unknown of their neighbours in the dales; and if they were hunters and robbers, perhaps they could pick up a living of a sort even now; but in old times when the land was waste, it was as good a place as could be for the home of wild half-savage fell-folk. The ground is not so high as to be bitterly cold in winter, and at a time when there were trees in plenty where now is only fern or heather, they could find cosy shelter. Down in the valley at that time everything was smothered up in wild wood, or uninhabitable for swamps and dampness, except where the ground had been cleared and drained by the hand of man. But high on the moors the ground drained itself; so that both for health and wealth it was the moor that was the chosen home of the earliest dwellers among the mountains; and their children lived on in the old places here and there, even after newcomers had begun to make their farms and villages where we see them nowadays.

Here at Heathwaite fell you can see the walls of their buildings, and even in little corners what may be chambers, or store-houses, or fire-spots, or what not, curiously built of great stones; but all quite different from the farm-buildings of our own people, and plainly the relics of an earlier race. Beside these stone walls there is one heap that is round and hollow in the midst, with a spot for a doorway, and well built within and without. Though the top of it is all fallen in, one can see that it might have been a hut shaped like a beehive, and roofed over with stone walling like those Pict-houses they tell of in other parts; this would be high enough inside for a big man to stand up in, and broad enough for him to lie at length. And all about the place there are the remains of huts ruder and more ancient than even this, though not of the kind that were made in the earliest ages of all, when folk used only stone tools. These show some knowledge of walling; and yet among them are plenty of graves where the fell-folk doubtless lie buried. At one end of this settlement, as they call it, there is a great barrow in which folk digging found burnt bones and you can see the tall stone that stood at the head still standing there. They call this place the Giant's Grave; and old neighbours tell that it is the burial place of the last of the giants who dwelt in that moorland village, and that he was shot with an arrow on that very fell side, and so was killed, and his race ended.

Well, when the big red man strode off through the heather and the ragged birches of the moor with Thorstein under his arm, this village was the spot he came to. He marched in at the gate of the intake, and up to the homestead through the cattle-folds with little cows of the old Northern breed and rough mountain goats, grazing between the walls; and through patches of kale and rye by the side of the tarn which lies blue and clear in the midst of the place. There in the evening sunshine, among the huts, would be a dozen or so of women and children, dirty and half-naked, both the old hags and the little goblins. They had four posts set upright in the earth, and a skin stretched over them in which was seething upon a fire of sticks a mess of flesh in its own broth. Some were making ready for the evening's feast, and some were cobbling

skins together : but for the most part they were a
set of idle do-noughts, to reckon by the filth and
hugger-mugger in which they lived.

They raised a screech when Thorstein was
brought in and cast on the ground : and set upon
him to stare at him and pull him about ; until
what with the raggedness of his torn clothes and
their handling he was mother-naked, and not a
little ashamed of his plight, and of his white skin.
Not that the fell-folk were blackamoors ; but they
were sunburnt with going half-naked, and grimy
with dirt. So there he sat, part covered with litter
and bracken which he pulled over himself ; and he
brazened it out as well as he could.

## CHAPTER XVII

## THORSTEIN'S BONDAGE

In a while the rest of the men came up, not all as huge as the giant who had caught him, but all long fellows, gaunt with fell-running and hard fare. They began their feast, dipping bowls and spoons into the skin over the fire, and drinking out of horns and cups until they were merry. Then one of the youngsters spied Thorstein where he sat, and threw at him the bone he had been gnawing. Thorstein warded it off with his hand, and others that were thrown : but whenever they hit him there was a horse-laugh. When all the bones were gnawed and thrown, one of them picked up a dart, which he threw at the lad : and it would have made an end of him, but Thorstein dodged it : at which they all cried " Oigh ! " and seemed to wonder at his address.

Last of all one of the men, seemingly enraged at his luck or cunning leaped up and ran at him with a cudgel, a thick stick with a stone hammer-head at the end of it. Thorstein had been through too much to cry out now : but what was his surprise when one of the children, a great girl with long red hair over her bare shoulders, ran in and flung her arms round him, half smothering him with her mane and the closeness of her embrace.

Then there was gabbling in a strange tongue while she kept him tight and seemed to forbid the giant lad to touch him : and the chief of them all spoke long, waving his arms and nodding his head, as who should say " Let the barn be, and we will keep him for our thrall." He seemed to show how he had threatened the lad with his own knife, and held up the knife, and pointed away over the fells : from which Thorstein gathered that they knew whence he had come and somewhat of who he was : and for the first time a gleam of hope shone into his heart.

In the end they gave him some of their meat, which he loathed and could not swallow : and pushed him into the stone hut, the best that there was, though even this could not be entered except by creeping : and they signed that he should lie down and go to sleep. But little sleep came to him : the place was filthy, and he was among unfriends ; his head ached and all his bones were sore. So he watched them as they came in one by one, and stripped, for the hut was as hot as an oven : and they lay down, as it seemed, in a heap, like snakes in an old tree root.

At last all was quiet without, and within they were snoring. The air was thick and foul : Thorstein could not breathe. It was fun to sleep in a tree with squirrels, but this was sleeping in a pighull among swine. He dragged himself like a worm, a little nearer the doorhole and then lay still,

After a while he dragged himself a little nearer : and lay still again, with his heart beating so loud, he feared it would awaken them all.

Out into the fresh air Thorstein crept in the end : and it was like a draught of cool ale after haymaking to taste the night wind. He stepped warily between the huts, straining his eyes in the gloom lest he should run against anything, for the night was cloudy and there were no stars, not even the dawn-streak in the north. He groped his way like a white ghost to the first wall, and began to climb it ; but just as he reached the coping, down it came with a rumble and a thud, and the stones fell on his feet and crushed them, so that he could not stir for the pain. And straightway he was in the grip of the giant again, who belaboured him with a dart, as if he had been a dog. The pain of his crushed feet and sickness was such that Thorstein felt little of the giant's blows, though every time the dart-head touched him, it cut into the bare flesh.

But when he woke up at last, it was in the nasty hut : and every one was gone except the child who had flown at him before ; and she was nursing his head and weeping over him. She looked so ugly, thought the boy, as he opened his eyes, with her face all blubbered and red, and the tears making dirty water-courses down her freckles, and dripping off her chin, and upon her rough red hair that hung all about. But when he came to himself, she called out shrilly, and an old woman brought milk in a pan and put it to the lad's mouth : and when he drank, the child let go his head to clap her hands and laugh. It hurt Thorstein to drop his head, but he thought she was less ugly when she laughed, and threw back her hair : and he saw that her eyes were blue, and her teeth shone. And it rested Thorstein when she took up his head again, and smiled and stroked him.

To make a short story, he lay there for days and nights, and sometimes slept, and often raved, and only now and then knew that the child was holding him and giving him drink from the milk-pan. Whether it was dark or light when he awoke from wild ugly dreams of swamps and snakes, and things chasing him through the brambles, and high endless walls to climb, and torrents of stones rolling down with him into the snakes again : whenever he came to his senses there she was, and no other pillow he had. In the end, the fever left him. As for his wounds they let the bark harden, and Thorstein had a whole skin before ever he was strong enough to stand up in it.

But when he could look about him, the child seemed to be eager in giving him what pleasure she could. She brought out a little kist that held her treasures : there were shining beads, and pennies of silver and gold with holes to hang them by, and a gold thing like a Thor's hammer, but Thorstein guessed it must be a cross ; for the child set it up and knelt down before it and prayed, looking sometimes at it and sometimes at him. Thorstein knew that his own people set little store by Christians, because they were not so good at fighting as the Northmen, and because they could be overreached by their chapmen, so they said : and he thought that all strange uncouth folk were Christians, as a matter of course : and so the wonder was less that giants and troll-kin in filthy huts should be of that faith.

But when he slept again after this awakening, he dreamed that he was at home, and his mother was kissing him good night, and stooping above him through the hangings of his own shut-bed : but her hair seemed to be all red like fern on the fells after early frost when the summer is over.

## CHAPTER XVIII

## RAINEACH

So Thorstein was healed of his sickness; but not until the summer was far spent, and not until he had begun little by little to learn words of the fell-folk's language. For whatever the child did for him or showed him she was not silent about it, but chattered the while, and often said its name loud and plain; and when he said it after her, she laughed and nodded. And Thorstein soon learnt with such teaching and never thought of being shy as children are when they are taught a strange tongue. What language she spoke, and what kind of people these were, you need not enquire too closely. They were not the Welsh, who still lived round about; nor were they Irish, for the Irish and Scottish thralls who have left their names on the map of these parts came in with their Norse masters, here as in Iceland. But these fells have always been a refuge; at all times there have been strangers hiding among them. In later days, down to living memory, smugglers and runaways have lived in the woods; and in ancient days deserters from a raiding troop or men fleeing from the justice or injustice of turbulent Strathclyde and Galloway no doubt wandered here, forebears of a little tribe that, when it died out, left no trace behind.

Now that he offered no longer to run away, they
treated him well after their fashion. He got the
cream of the milk, as if he had been a chief's son at
fostering : although the cream was always sour
from keeping in foul crocks of rough clay ; and
indeed they liked it so, as though new cream were
tasteless. There was always plenty of flesh meat,
of roe-deer and hares and other savoury sorts, good
enough, said he to himself, if one doesn't watch the
cooking. As the saw says " What the eye never
sees the heart never grieves after," so their clarty
ways vexed him less and less, as the days wore, and
as Greenodd began to be like a dream on the other
side of awakening.

Lying in the hut, or sitting out in the sun
wrapped in a deer-skin, Thorstein watched the
people and when they were not so new to him they
seemed less strange and uncouth. Even when the
men came in, whereas at first he crept as far out of
the way as he could, at last he was drawn to look
on at the game they brought, red-deer and roe-deer,
wild boar and hares, all manner of moor-fowl and
mere-fowl, and wonderful fish, spotted trout, and
silver and golden char, whose pink flesh is the
delicatest of all eating. Thorstein had seen some
little sport at Greenodd, but it was plain that there
the great lake was a teeming fish-pond and the great
fells one deer-park, and that these red men were the
cunningest of hunters and fishers, if their farming
was nought.

Nor were they rough with him now. Once,
when a huge youngster began to tease him with

some more horse-play, the giant carle who was father and chief of them all, laid open the lout's head for him. And if once he had thought that they had no manners, and their customs were beastly, now he began to find that they were cunning in their own craft, eloquent in their own tongue, kind to their own kin, and proud of their own havings. It was not always growls and blows: many a time the little wench would play with her ugly father, and cuddle him prettily, and he would pet her as if, said Thorstein to himself, they were no Christian savages, but decent Thor-fearing folk. And if he had looked down upon them as the dirt beneath his feet, he now gathered that they reckoned less of him than he thought for, and kept him at arm's length while they treated him well, just as a boy treats a squirrel he has caught, stroking it while he holds it hard, for fear it should bite.

So the summer wore and the autumn came, and Thorstein was kept within walls or close at hand. He spent his time with the women for the most part, helping them in their work, but much as he liked. They let him stack wood for fires : sew and fashion such garments as they made from skins, or from cloth that they got by barter for pelts. Sometimes he was let milk the cows and goats, and take them to pasture ; but then there was always somebody to watch that he should not run away. Other whiles he tried his hand at woodwork : but it was long before they let him handle a knife, and when they did, sharp eyes were upon him all the time. But they seemed mighty pleased when he turned out little stools and boxes, pegged together with wooden nails, or bits of hooper's work that would hold water, And as he began to be useful, so he got on famously with them and felt homelike.

The child who had nursed him gave him to understand that her name was Raineach (you might call her " Rannie ") that is Fern : and indeed she was not unlike the bracken when it is red in autumn, and she was slender and strong and wild as its tall fronds that smother up the hollows among the boulders on the moors. She was maybe a year or so younger than Thorstein, but as tall as he. Gartnaidh mac Tairneach, which is the Son of Thunder, was the name of her father, the giant as we may call him, for he was a head and shoulders taller than even a tall fellow among the Northmen, and far away bigger than the Welsh. Raineach was pleased when she found out Thorstein's name and what it meant in her talk ; for it is as much as to say the Thunderstone, because Thor is nothing else than the Thunder-god. " And so," said she, " We are brother and sister, for the Thunder-stone is the Thunder's child." And Thorstein by this time was little loath to have it so : and whenever his mind went to Greenodd it took Raineach there too, and he could see her in his dreams in their hall, sharing his trencher and cup, and friendly with Hundi, and tormented by Orm. So he put off the escape that sometimes he planned, until he might persuade her to run with him.

But when at last he had words enough to open out his mind, and to tell her of his longing for home, she was astonished and grieved, and gave him to know that she thought him a very lucky lad to be living in such good company and so well off as he was. For many days she was cool with him and said little : which angered him, so that he would say nothing to her. Once when they were out with the goats together, and she was groping in a blackberry bush, a wild cat sprang straight out at her, like a shot from a sling : and fixed teeth and claws all together in her shoulder. Thorstein had the creature throttled in an instant, but great work it was to get it off, and to kill it, bang as he might with his thick stick. And then he got her home, and the women put herbs on the bite to take the poison out, and to stop the blood. So it was Thorstein's turn to be nurse for a while, and his sulkiness melted away : all the more that she gave a fine story of his bravery.

Which when the giant heard, he said the little fellow was good enough now to go out with the men. And after that, for many a weary day and through many a terrible night, trotted he behind long-shanks and his lads by moor and mire, chasing the red deer and the roe, and snaring the fowl of wild-wood and water. And one while he got good words for his work ; and other whiles, for all he could do, it was nought but ill luck, and an empty belly, and hard blows to his back. But to such doings one hardens when limbs are young, and each time the weariness and the danger are forgotten. Hunger and cold, and rough companionship, and the squalor of the huts became too common to be feared any more. And as the months passed, the boy waxed and throve in the keen air of the fells. He grew cunning to track the slot, keen of eye and deft of hand, like any savage of them all : and Raineach was proud of her foster-brother.

## CHAPTER XIX

## THE THREE TASKS

WHEN Thorstein had found his tongue and could talk to the fell-folk in their own speech, he would often tell Raineach about Greenodd and his home.

Sometimes in the winter weather, as they were crouching by the open-air fire in sleet and wind to dress their meals, or cowering in the foul huts from the storms that swept the moor, there would come before him, like a dream, the bonny eld-house and its beloved rafters, and the bright things gleaming on the wainscot, and the lasses in their neat kirtles a-spinning or a-sewing; his mother with her needle, and his father with woodsmith's tools, and all so cosy and well-to-do as they worked and sang in the warm fireshine.

Then he would whisper to the giant's lass, as they huddled together in the muck, and the men growled or snored—for there was little to do in the winter up there but sleep it out like bears—and he would say, " Raineach, I see them, I see them ! There's our great dog asleep with his nose on the edge of the hearth, and father is kicking the logs together, and he pats the dog and says to mother, ' Where's poor old Stein now ? I wonder if he's all right somewhere, or tanning his hide in a cold peat-pit.' Mother shakes her head at Hundi and

says, ' Eh, lad, it was a bad day thou tookest him
off : the elder should have been the wiser.' For
I'll uphold it Hundi has led a hound's life ever
since. But I can see mother working flowers on a
kirtle, and she has been working at it every day this
back-end : blue flowers, Raineach, and gold leaves
on a brave red stuff : eh, if you saw what I see, you
would see some bonny things and all.

" And the chapmen will be coming about, with
packs full of wares from all the round world, and
they'll be feasting them. And at Yule, what
doings ! Pies, lass, as big as anthills : and butter
to thy haver-bread, and honey in thy porridge :
and laiks in the afternoons, when the tables are
cleared and folk pull skins across the fire, and one
side lets go and down they tumble : and one is
blindfolded and hunts the others : and I'd show
thee a safe place, Raineach, so that they couldn't
catch thee. How thou'd laugh, and how they'd
laugh : and how we'd sing and tell stories, and get
eh, that frightened, and then mother would say
' Barns to bed,' and we'd pull the clothes over our
heads while we heard their goings-on. Grand
it would be if I could get thee there to peep in on
them all."

With such talk, Raineach, who had looked on
Thorstein as a poor savage at first, came to feel a
great longing to see what wonderful things might
be yonder across the fells : and once even asked her
father whether they could not pay a visit to
Thorstein's folk at Greenodd. She said they
would come back again, never fear : and maybe

bring some of the things Thorstein told her of. Gartnaidh laughed at first ; then he growled, and shook his fist at the lad, and bade him say no more to the child. And for a good while they found it hard to come together : there was always something for her to do, and something for him elsewhere : and life was worse than before.

At last when spring came, Thorstein plucked up his courage and said boldly that he wanted to go home.

" Well, my little man," says the giant, " here we have nursed thee for a summer and a winter, and given our best : and what," says he, " shall we get for a parting gift ? for it is little we have got as yet."

Thorstein said that his father would be sure to give something.

" Nay," says the carle, " I know him and his gifts."

Thorstein reddened and bit his lips.

" Now," says the giant, " do this for me, and I'll let thee go : keep my cattle this twelve-month, and see them well served : but if one be missing thy head shall pay for it."

So the lad became herdboy to the fell-folk : and well he knew his job, for he had been among the beasts at home, and was used to all that belonged to cattle. But these were well-nigh wild, and bad, bad to manage. Often they would break bounds, and give him a rough job to hunt them out of the mires and woods, where wolves might get them before ever they had time to be lost. And many a night it was only by the help of the lass that he could gather them together and drive them into the fold for the milking : and sometimes it seemed that an unfriendly hand would loose them, and give him a sad scare. But Raineach managed so that in a while the rest of the folk were ashamed or afraid to meddle. And they throve that summer, and after the slaughtering at the back end of it, Thorstein kept as many as would make up his count for the spring : and was diligent in serving them with everything he could lay hands on. So the end of it was that when winter was near spent he delivered over his full tale to the carle, and bade him farewell.

"Not so fast, my little fellow," said the giant. "I reckon nought of this. Here are all my beasts again, no doubt : but what more ? We are no better off than we were."

"What then ? " cried the lad, aghast.

"This," said the carle. "Seest yonder tarn ? When it is as yellow with corn as it is blue to-day, we will talk more of this matter : but if I hear another word, it will be the word for knocking thy brains out with this club of mine." And he dashed about him with his great oaken cudgel in a way that was grewsome.

So Thorstein was angry and mad angry : and in his anger set himself to bail the water out of the tarn the giant had pointed to—one of a many there were in those days about Heathwaite, though now they are all peated up, without it be Pewit tarn. Then Raineach came and stood by ; and when she saw the water trickling back into the pool, and the rain beating into it, and the sweat running off the lad's face, she laughed. He asked her what she was laughing at : and she said, " At thee." Then he threw at her the crock that he was bailing with, and bad her begone for a heartless wretch. But she drew back, and it fell on a stone and was broken : at which she laughed the more. Then he sat down and wept. And she came to him in the rain and comforted him, and called him a fool, which is often the best comfort from one that can help.

" Look," she said, " silly lad, how the water runs out of the broken pot. Break the tarn, and it will be dry."

" Nay, I know that well enough," said he.

" Well, do it," said she.

" But how ? " said he.

Then she showed him that the rock ran in ridges, and that he might dig the earth away between the ridges and make a beck. So he dug the earth and made a beck : but still there was water in the tarn.

" Who is the fool, now ? " said he.

" Not I," said she : " throw upon the tarn all the earth out of the digging, and fill it up."

Thorstein thought she was a clever lass, and threw all the stones he could find, and a deal of earth upon them into the tarn ; and if it was somewhat miry, it was no tarn any longer. But now he was let down for seed to sow : and beg as he might, they said they had but enough for themselves. Then after some days of bitter words and

nights of useless thinking, came Raineach with a
bag full of corn. She would not tell whence it
came, but it was good seed corn : and Thorstein
sowed it, and watched it morn and eve, and built a
fence around to keep man and beast out of it. And
glad he was when it showed above the brown
earth, and fain when the ears began to turn yellow :
and bade the giant see to it, and let him go forthwith. But all he got was a growl and a roar.

" Where did that corn come from ? "

" Not from thee," says Thorstein.

" Thief ! " says the giant.

" Liar ! " says Thorstein : and they were both as
angry as they might be. But the giant would not
kill him, and best knew the reason why. For he
meant to keep the lad against a time when there
should be trouble with the Northmen, and then
give him over as a ransom. So he was in no
hurry to let his prisoner go.

" Look you here," says the giant at last : " those
great firs yonder where the crows build—they
must be cut down and made into a house for me
before ever I let thee go."

" Ask another to do the job," said Thorstein.

" Never another will I ask," said the giant :
" folk that can make corn grow in tarns, can make
firs into houses."

So Thorstein toiled at one of the least of the trees
with his knife and a little hatchet, the best he could
find : but he could only notch it round, and it
stood as straight as ever. Then Raineach came
and laughed at him again, and bade him go to sleep

till she helped him : but she would not say how or when. And in a while she disappeared altogether.

One day when nobody was nigh, the men all away hunting, and Thorstein bewailing himself, he looked at the firwood from afar, and thought one of the tree tops shook more than the wind used to shake it. By and by it fell, and he heard a crash in the wood. He ran down to the spot, and there was a great tree on the ground and chips of new-cut wood all about it : but never a soul to be seen. Then the lass came laughing, and saying it was magic, and the good folk would have none of his spying ; and so she took him by the shoulders and pushed him out of the wood. Magic or no magic, she managed that on certain days the men were out early and home late, and none of them noticed that the fir tops were gone : and Thorstein was hugely puzzled. At last he went to the spot by stealth, and saw strange men working there : they looked like Welsh, and he guessed they might be from across the flats. They had many of the trees down, and sawed and squared into timbers, that men might carry on their shoulders. Raineach was not there ; but round the neck of the foreman of them, as it seemed, was her gold cross hanging. Then the lad knew how she had helped him : and right proud he was of her and her favours, and told her as much.

So when the winter was on them, one day comes Thorstein up with a plank on his shoulder, and " Where is thy house to stand ? " says he to the giant,

" What ! " cries the giant, " who felled my trees ? "

" They are felled," says the lad.

" Not by thee," says the giant.

" That's neither here nor there," says Thorstein : " where is the house to stand ? "

The giant was not ill pleased to think he was to have a house like the Northmen, and so he let things be : and Raineach made the lads of the fell-folk help, in that they dragged up the big timbers right merrily, and Thorstein was master of the works. And if his building was not great nor very workmanlike, it was game to him when the studs were sunk in the ground, and beams hoisted and fixed with pegs, and rafters began to show the shape of the roof. And all this was done with the tools left in the wood by the strangers, of whom nothing could be heard. Most folk said it was fairies.

## CHAPTER XX

### *OVER THE FELLS*

BEFORE the building of the house was done, in the
early spring when Thorstein had been now three
winters among the red folk, there was once more
rumour of war throughout all the north, and the
sound of it came even to these wildernesses, so far
as they were apart from the dwellings and inter-
course of men.   For Gartnaidh the giant, being in
this respect like Swein Biornson, was a borderer
and a dweller on no man's land, that is to say he had
no laws nor kings over him, and was bound to no
government of lawmakers.   And yet he was akin
to others dwelling up and down these parts : who,
though they were at ancient feud with their Welsh
neighbours, yet could let sleeping dogs lie when it
served their turn, and play at give and take, or
even do good work for Owain the king of Cumbria.
For since these hardy hunters and fell runners knew
the lie of the land better than settled ploughmen or
townsfolk, in many ways they were useful, as in
guiding the Northmen to Dacre, and in spying
upon them often, when little they knew what eyes
were gleaming through the green leafage.   Add to
this that Gartnaidh and his like found the king's
service not unprofitable ;  and poor folk must live,
however proud they be.

So when war was talked of, the news came to their ears somehow, handed on from one to another of the woodlanders, or picked up at market; for there were times when they came in to sell their furs to the Welsh or Anglians at burgs and trading places on the outskirts of the mountains, as at Ravenglass or Cartmel.

This time it seemed certain that the north was going to rise against the south in good earnest. Constantine and Olaf Cuaran, Owain and the new Dublin king Olaf Guthferthson had made common cause. Says the giant to Thorstein, " Thy folk will be gathering at their meeting-place in the mountains, and that is hard by our meeting-place too. Thither I am going, and if thou hast a mind to see thy father—"

" Say no more," cried Thorstein : and they made ready for the journey.

In those days, to one who knew the country, the best roads were not always down below, but the tops and ridges of the fells. The valleys were all umbered up with trees, or choked with swamps ; and what with wild beasts and what with wild folk, travelling was no child's play. But in the waste wildernesses of high moorland, on the tall rock ranges that joined peak to peak like bridges in the air, foe in shape of mankind was hardly to be found. It was rough work over snow in winter and through moss and mire in summer-time, and a stranger would easily be lost and never seen again : but these hunters were at home anywhere between Skiddaw and Black Comb,

Gartnaidh the giant, with Thorstein and a few of the lads that followed him, were not far on their way, when there was a stir in the woods behind them, and presently through the coppice came a slim running figure, in brogues and tightly knit plaid and deer-skin, and a great bush of red hair streaming behind.

" How now, Raineach ? " says the giant : " what folly is this ? We want no wenches on this journey."

With that she pouted, and when he bade her turn back, she began to weep, and sat down on a stone to lament. Thorstein was vexed to see her cry, and would have stayed by her to comfort her : for indeed it had been a sore parting but a little while before. Then the giant took him by the elbow and shoved him along the road, telling him not to be a fool, or never a sight of his father would he get.

Well, they went along for a space : and as they climbed one height of the many on that moorland around what we call Beacon tarn, where the lad used to fish with the lass : and while he was thinking that after all they were happy days he was leaving behind : just then, one of them cried out that there was a stir again in the birch boughs on the height they had left : and a red spot flitted over the heather from cover to cover. Gartnaidh bade the man shoot an arrow to scare their follower : and the man shot, but took good care to aim wide.

They pushed on, until they were out of their own grounds, so to say, and nearing Coniston. As the travellers came towards the place, along the brow between Banniside and the lake, there was a shout in the rear, and a scream which they could not but understand. So they ran back on their traces, and soon saw Raineach fighting and kicking in the grip of a rough fellow, who made off when he saw the big men. It was little use to scold her, and too late to carry her back home. Gartnaidh said no more when she came up with them, and only strode on with his best foot foremost, so that it was all she could do to trot after and keep in sight, for many a weary hour.

From Coniston they slanted up great crags until they got to the top of the high waterfall we call the White Lady, because she comes and goes like a wraith. Thence they found their way over the bogs to Wetherlam cove and the head of the great gill that runs down into Yewdale. Then away they went up and down over the rough fells, until they found lodging for the night in Mickleden, with some who had their huts there. The children were right glad to rest their swollen and battered feet on a heather-heap all night, whether asleep or awake, while the men talked loud round the fire.

The morning it was up and away over wilder ground than ever, climbing by the ledges of rock to the bogs that make as it were a thatched roof above the walls of those great mountain houses, whose streets are the dales, and whose gables are the peaks. All day long it was wading through the mosses, or clambering over the screes, up and down long slopes that seemed in the passing clouds and showers to lead nowhither but into the rain and the mist. In the afternoon they were aware of a great valley beneath them. They had come so to say to the eaves of the house of mountains and yet could not look over, nor see what was going on below. But they were above the dale through which the old path goes, beneath Helvellyn and by the lake of Thirlmere, where Elphin the Roman used to haunt.

There, as Gartnaidh reckoned, there would be some force posted to defend the border and the road to the south, for it would be a likely point of attack. With this point guarded, and the coast road, and the middle way that comes through the Westmorland fells, king Owain would be safe, and free to throw his whole power upon York by the great way over Stainmoor. And it was thought that the king himself might soon be there, to speak about the defences with the people of the place, and with the Northmen who would be coming to meet him.

But Gartnaidh had no mind to put his daughter in the way of Owain's soldiers, any more than to leave her in the clutches of the ruffian on Banniside : neither would he give Thorstein the chance of getting away before his time. So he avoided the Welsh burg at Wythburn, and led them down upon a dwelling of his kindred, such as dwelt here along the brink overlooking Thirlmere, on the Benn as we still call it in their language—the great mountain between Armboth and Thirlmere water-foot.

## CHAPTER XXI

## *ALUINN*

DOWN came they through the bracken, which was just beginning to shoot among the boulders of the moor, and were stopped by a group of men who seemed to have sprung out of the ground; and indeed for colour and rough aspect they seemed to be part and parcel of it, as paddocks match mud and caterpillars mimic twigs of trees. A shout in the fell-folk's tongue put all to rights without fighting; and then they saw two low houses on the slope of the moor, built of great stones and roofed over with peat. They passed by these to the head of a gill that ran sharp down between cut rocks, and then they found more of these houses. There were people about, who welcomed them when they knew who the visitors were, and came out of the huts, unkempt and fierce as Gartnaidh's folk, and yet as proud as he in their mountain fastness.

It was built on a nab between two ravines, and the only path ran steeply down to the wath across Thirlmere. From this spot one could see the length of the lake and all its rugged shores, cleft into scars and steeps, and whatever was not rock or water was trees. Over against them was the great wall of Helvellyn, rising high, and seemingly sheer and unattainable in the clouds of heaven. Such steepness and such dizzy terror of falling the children had never known, as when they came to the utmost of the houses, which stood on the nab, where on either hand and in front the ground fell suddenly away, as when one stands on a high tower, and men are like mice underneath one's feet. A woman kept house in this place, not old, but no longer young; tall, and sinewy in her arms, with beautiful fair hair: but a harsh face, and a harsh voice. She welcomed Gartnaidh, and said little to the children, but did them no harm, and gave them a better supper than they were used to have on Heathwaite fell. For though the cot was rude, she seemed to have plenty, and there were neighbours, and the road was below, by which a sort of marketing could now and then be done if one had the means; whereas at Raineach's home neither love nor money could get what was never there to be got.

When they had eaten, out they crept as children do, to see the new place they had come to: and looked over the brink into the gill with its soft moss and purple butterwort cushioning all the rough hard rocks, and sweetfern fringing the fountains that sprayed into dimpling basins among the stone, or slid down black slopes under a roof of silky-barked birch and white-flowering rowan. Here and there ancient gnarled hawthorn-trees clung to the crags: one especially was thick with may-blossom, as if it were loaded with snow: its rich almond scent hung about the place, coming and going like a breath.

The children scrambled down the steep side to get at its boughs from above, for it grew close to the slope, like a flower in a girl's bosom. But when they broke a hole as it were in the white thatch, what should they see but the loveliest lady in the world sitting among the twisted boughs, and the finest prince in the world, as it seemed to them, standing below, and reaching out his arms to her, and speaking passionately, with his eyes afire and bonny smooth cheeks aglow. But when he saw the strange little faces thrust through the blossom-roof, with wide opened mouths and staring eyes like goblins, he slid away with a start, down the forest slope, like a snake in the whins, so that they could just see the flash of his belt and the glint of red and blue in the leafage as he disappeared. And when they looked again for the lovely lady, she was gone.

They were too astonished to say a word, but Thorstein held Raineach's hand, and they climbed back to the cot, and crept in, bidden to sleep by the woman of the place. It was not long before something bright was at the door ; and in came the lovely lady they had seen, with grey eyes wide open as if she saw wonders, and a smile that stirred their heart-strings, and all her golden hair flaming about her green gown.

The woman—they could only be mother and daughter—looked at her quickly ; and looked at her again : and even Gartnaidh, who had not yet gone away, bent his brows upon her in amazement. Then he made one of those clumsy reverences of his, for he had at whiles a sort of half forgotten courtesy about him, like a man who has seen better days. "So this is thy lovely daughter," said he. "When I saw Elphin map Rhydderch, the worthy lord warden of the march, roll in the dust, little did I think what sweet flower would have sprung from such a dunghill."

"Peace," said the woman. "And thou, Aluinn, what news?"

"News?" said the beautiful girl. "Grand news! Nay, what news should there be?"

"Fool," said the mother. "Greet thy kinsman Gartnaidh mac Tairneach and give word of thine errand."

She kissed the big red man on the beard, and stood thinking: and said "Ah, the king's men have come, if that be all."

"Well?" said her mother and Gartnaidh.

"Oh, a good troop; maybe three score, maybe six score. I forget."

"And the king?"

"Oh, aye, the king, I suppose, and the young ·king, I suppose: and all as it should be. But oh mother, the hawthorn is sweet to-night, and the birds are wild with their singing, and I was fain to bide out in the gill. It was bad of me, for I should have been here serving the company. Is our good kinsman suppered? Where are his folk? What can I do to help thee?" and she began as if to busy herself with the housekeeping.

"Peace, child," said the mother. "Gartnaidh mac Tairneach is served, and for his folk, they are

I

bestowed. Two of them, hush, they are asleep."

But Thorstein and Raineach, vaguely bethinking them of manners little learned on Heathwaite fell, sat up on the heather heap in the corner which was their bed. Aluinn started at the two goblin faces, the red head and the tow head, unkempt and uncouth, rising in the dark corner; and she screamed and laughed wildly.

" What's to do with the silly thing now?" cried the woman, and shook her : but all she got was a flood of tears.

Gartnaidh was mightily aggrieved that his children should be taken for goblins, and all manner of talk was held, as Aluinn came to her right mind : and said she was sick, and lay down in her bed. And so they all rested, uneasily enough, for that night.

In the morning she was quite another lass, and chattering like a jay. Raineach her young kinswoman was made much of, and if she stared shyly at the wonderful beauty for half a day, she was won over into companionship by the afternoon. The lad was ill at ease : he could not tell why, for nobody spoke him aught but fair. Gartnaidh was away to the king's army : and now and again there were sounds of stirring below, as if horns were blown far down through the forest, and men shouted.

Thorstein moped about, staring at the great mountains half hidden by rain and mist, while the two lasses foregathered. He came in and helped his hostess with her tasks, but she looked at him askance. He had never felt more a stranger, even in his first days among the fell-folk. At bed-time, the beautiful Aluinn turned to him and waved her hand. "Lads lie there:" she said. "Raineach is my bed-fellow."

Thorstein crept into the place she pointed at. It was a little tiny shed at the end of the hut: a sort of kist of stone walling, just high enough to crawl into, and long enough to lie in: a dog-kennel or fowl-house it might have been. But the heather was soft within, and he crept out and gathered more, and piled it around him.

Early in the morning, he was awakened. Raineach's face was at his feet, peeping in through the door-hole. "Heigh!" she said, whispering loud and eagerly. "Thorstein, listen! I know it all. The bonny man is the king's son. Wake, Thorstein! Aluinn wears his gold collar round her neck: I saw it when she doffed her clothes. And she gave him her ring. Thou wilt give me a gold collar, Thorstein? Wake up, lad! And thy father killed her father, think of that! He was a wicked man, and they were glad. But Domhnall is a lovely man. And if thy father hadn't killed her father, she would be a lady at the Castle down there. Domhnall is the king's son, Thorstein: and Aluinn will be queen, Thorstein. Oh poor Thorstein, they said thou wast a wolf's cub: but I said nay. Now, thou must have a red coat, and I would have thine eyes shine like—"

"Go away!" growled the lad from his lair.

## CHAPTER XXII

### THORSTEIN SEES HIS
### FATHER

Now all this while Thorstein was eager for a sight of his father : why else was he here ? And all the more because his heart was sore against Raineach who could so lightly leave him for her fine friend. He bethought him, little as he knew of love-making, that he must cap yon glittering Welshman, or else be cast off as a good-for-nought and a lout. There was only one way of doing this : namely to get back among his own people, and let it be seen what like they were, and what like was he when his hand was in its glove again.

Down yonder he knew was the path and the wath across the water. Run he could and swim : why not away ? So he slipped off and slid down the gill, steep and steeper down the great crags beneath the fell-folk's houses, and buried deep and dark in trees that covered the brink on both hands with well-nigh impassable thickets. Down the cliff he went, holding by tuft and ledge, and at last let himself go, sliding down the scree with a fall that brought him to the brink of the waterfall.

It was a black basin of rock into which the white foam tumbled through the ferns, a secret place among rowan and hawthorn. In the splashing water lay great rocks, some as it were bits of carven pillars six-sided, and others whose fragments were bright with red and green colours, and curiously inlaid with patterns of white and black that looked like lace work. They seemed to be the precious stones folk put in rings and brooches only larger and more precious in every way. He picked them out of the water, and broke them smaller to get the glowing bits out, thinking what fine jewellery he had lit upon; there would be enough for more than Raineach could wear, aye, and for every one he knew; and maybe gold might be found where jewels were, if he could but light upon it.

He hunted stones up and down the gill until he was wearied, not to say bruised and bleeding with his scrambling among the sharp rocks and with many a fall in dub and force: so he lay down, wet as he was, beside his heaped treasure, and slept. But when he awoke, the bright colours on the stones had all faded: they shone only while they were lying in the water, and against the black and grey of the wild rocks in the gill. The white hawthorn and the purple butterwort were brighter by far, and faded not so soon as the fairy colours of these stones.

Then he bethought him to explore the gill and find his way down to the lake: for every beck comes to dale at last. But this was no beck like the streams of the lower moorlands. It was all fierce forces with rocks on either hand, and when the

ground was ever so little passable the trees had got a
hold of it, and hedged it up. And yet he won
down, and lighted upon the road that led to the
wath. Then came folk. Thorstein went back
into the wood, for he dared not risk being seen in
broad daylight. He forced his way up the brow
of the fell aslant through the trees, and struck a path
that brought him to the houses above.

So the long day wore, and the gloaming came
late as it does in Lakeland in midsummer : but it
came : and the lasses were abroad, and the woman
throng with her house-keeping in the cot. He
slipped away down the gill again and found the
road, and stood awhile wondering whether he
should swim the lake or go boldly by the general
fording-place. Then there was a noise of horses
and men. He climbed a hammer, a jutting rock
that overhung the road, and lay down flat upon it to
see and not be seen.

The troop of way-farers came on in silence, as
wearied men who had travelled far between
morning and this late twilight-time, on wearied
beasts—ponies we should call them rather than
horses : for the nags they rode in those days were
tiny compared with the great chargers of the
knights in after ages. It was grey mirk by now,
and only when they came close beneath him did
Thorstein know them for Northmen. But even so
their mailcoats and their fighting helms of iron,
with great leather flaps, disguised them. He crept
nearer to the edge to look over. A stone fell from
under him and one of them passing beneath looked

up sharply. "Father, father!" cried the lad; but at that very instant was gripped from behind, and throttled fiercely, and dragged up into the wood: with two great hands round his neck, and a knee in his back to hold him down, quick or dead.

Beneath, upon the road, there was a scurrying to and fro, as Swein Biornson swore it was his lad's voice, and he would know it anywhere.

"Nay, man, it was but an owl," said some: and others upheld that it was some trick to draw them into ambushment: or maybe a troll of that hag-ridden wilderness. Swein climbed the hammer, where nothing was to be seen or heard, but the roar of the beck in the gill, and a grisly groaning in the wood, that might be wind in the trees, or wood-sprites, or what not. So they went forward, none the slower for this adventure: and the sound of them died in distant pattering.

"Ha, my little wolf-cub," said the giant Gart-naidh, loosing his grip of Thorstein's throat: "so thou hast eyes for thy father, and none for thy foster-father. Well, what was my promise? That thou shouldst see him: and thou hast seen him. Good: we art quits. Now no more straying of nights, dog. Get to thy kennel." And he drove him through the woods with many a stripe, and kicked him into his lair, and rolled a big stone against the hole of it.

## CHAPTER XXIII

## DOMHNALL

So there we leave Thorstein to bite his hands and weep for that slip between cup and lip, the bitterest he had known. Gartnaidh came into the cot, and what should he see but Raineach, giggling and wide-eyed over a silken scarf that a gay spark, he knew him well, was tying round her bare shoulders : and the house-mistress smiling and becking and bowing like a fool. Aluinn was not there : but they seemed merry, and the wild lass looked quite bonny in the firelight.

"What, goodfellow giant!" said Domhnall, with somewhat shame-faced bravery, as Gartnaidh scowled in at them; "here we are all as merry as hares by moonlight; and upon my honour, I make my best bow to the father of such a bright little thing."

"See what he has given me," said Raineach with childish pride.

"She'll be back before long," said the mother. "I warrant now I know of it, Aluinn just slipped away to look for somebody. But take something, sir. It's little we fell-folk have to offer the likes of you : though fair's the day that brought you : and it's a poor place for a king's son, though the last drop of Roman blood runs in the veins of our Aluinn."

"It's the sweetest spot in the world, mother," said Domhnall : "and no finer greeting can I give you when we take our Aluinn to court, and all the lords of the land have to bow down before her."

Then Aluinn burst in, breathless and haggard and panting. She flew at her lover, and held him tight, taking no heed of them all.

"What now ? " cried they, and the young man unwound her arms from his neck, and held her off a little.

They learnt bit by bit that she had strayed out to look for him, and away on the road toward the wath. She had hidden while a troop of men rode past—Northmen they would be, going to their meeting place. She had heard them splash over the ford, and then it was dark and she turned homewards. But suddenly she saw a light, as if some wayfarer were camping in the wood by the lake-side. It brightened and spread, until she thought the forest was on fire. But no sound of crackling branches or hissing flame could she hear. The blaze grew broader ; sparks flew on high, and all round it seemed one great flickering. Then she was terrified and fled by the well-known wood-paths, daring no more to look behind her.

The men went out to a little spying-place on the uttermost brink of the nab, but fire there was none. The glow of the Northmen's camp was hidden behind Great Howe, and the Welsh burg was away beyond the crags.

" Why, pretty one," said Domhnall, coming in,
" what fancies are these? The heather's afire I
know, for all the country is up: but that is the only
blaze, and black night it is between here and
Helvellyn."

" But I saw it," said the lass shuddering.

" It was only a glint of moonshine: come, little
silly, let us be merry again."

" Nay," said her mother thoughtfully, and stood
up, tall and strange. " She saw it. I have seen it.
Twice before I have seen it, and well I know the
sight. Once for death: and again for death: and
the third time."

" Come, good mother," said Domhnall, " never
seek to scare us. King's sons and queens that are
to be, give no heed to old wives' soothsayings.
Aluinn, smile now, and drink. It will do thee
good, and me too."

" Peace, young man," said the mother. " Are
not all thy men now bound for battle, and un-
appeasable war with the great king? Which of
them all, think'st thou, which of them that drink
to-night and shout drunkenly round their fires, will
come unscathed out of the fire of the fight, to
march hitherward again in triumph to the homes of
their fathers and their children? Nay, I tell you,
not a man of them all. And which of them will lie
in agony on the desolate heath far away in Saxon-
land, till the ravens pluck out their eyes, and the
wolves tear their hearts out of the riven harness?
Aye, by that token, many and many a one. I see
them there, the proudest, the mightiest, the bravest;

I see them in their blood : and I see the handful
that flee over heath and hill, in their shame and
their sorrow, terror-stricken before the sword of
England and trembling beneath the spear of the
stranger, fleeing to their lairs in the mountains and
to all the wild-wood fastnesses : and I hear the wail
of the mourner, and the scream of the captive, and
the curse of the mother that bore the coward and
the coward's son."

"Ah, my life, go not out to this battle," cried
Aluinn, clinging to him. "Stay by us in peace :
and if evil must come, let it roll over thy head,
lying hidden here in safety."

"What ! " said Domhnall, " shirk the play for a
girl's vision and a woman's fears ? "

"King," said Gartnaidh, " for thou, lord,
may'st be king before this moon has waned—these
are no idle counsels. A brave heart is the praise of
youth, but a seeing eye is the glory of a king. Hear
me. Gartnaidh mac Tairneach is no coward, but
he is old : and life is good to him in the woods : is
it not good to thee in the city and in the court ?
And if blood must be shed, why should the blood of
father and son redden one field together ? Stay by
us here, and claim from king Owain the wardenship
of these marches. It is a post of honour. And so
we shall keep the seed corn while we spend the
reapings of the harvest."

Thus they talked until morning, and it was
resolved that Domhnall, nothing loath, for the sake
of Aluinn if not to save his own skin, should withhold himself from the battle. Gartnaidh, because

he knew the land, and was cunning as a spy, got the
ear of King Owain next day ; and saying nothing of
the vision, bade the king go in peace, and begged
that Domhnall might be left with the defenders of
the border, to keep them in heart, and to be king of
the land in his father's room, to do justice upon the
upstarts and peacebreakers, who always showed
their heads when the king's back is turned.   Such
advice was held to be good, and the army went on
its way to fight Athelstan at Brunanburg.

## CHAPTER XXIV

### THE GIANT'S CASTLE

CLEAN gone were the Welshmen at last, and the Northmen with them; and then came Gartnaidh and dragged poor Thorstein out of his lair, where he had lain a night and a day with little ease: and took his daughter with them: and over the mosses they travelled, no long way, to the stronghold where the fell-folk were used to retire in times of war and trouble. All along the Benn their houses were scattered, but on the side away from Thirlmere there is a deep valley. No wilder might be in any part, and scarcely in any land inhabited, than this that opens at Shoulthwaite. On either side high cliffs, brant and broken, rise above the sheets of ruin, which fall from them among scanty leafage of battered forest-trees. In one place the crags frown over the gill as they frown nowhere else in our fells, overhanging their bases, as if they would topple down with a breath. The gill is steep and rocky; the chasm that cleaves its sides, one long waterfall from top to bottom, coming down from the high moors and desolate bogs to the low-lying valley and inhabited plain between the Benn and Blencathra.

There in the midst of this trough runs out a

tongue of land, steep on either side : and the tip of it rises abrupt into a tall rocky island, precipitous all round, and approachable only by a narrow neck that joins it to the mountain.

Across this neck great trenches had been dug in ancient times, deep and wide, and curving round the castle rock, like the new moon lying about the old. So huge they are that they remain there to this day. And if the first is climbed there is the second ; and if the second is climbed there is the third, twice as high ; and no way to circumvent it or avoid it if one would get up to the stronghold in the midst. And then there is the hollow in the rock where a few houses might be built, as the forecourt of the castle or its outer bailey, defended on two sides by the sheer precipice, and on the third by the trenches : but on the fourth side rises still higher the uttermost rock, a rugged tower unapproachable save by a narrow path like a ledge in the side of it, so that one only at once can enter ; and one man above with a good spear could easily defend it, thrusting each new comer over in turn, and down into the gulf below, like sheep one by one thrust into the pool at a sheep-washing. Then on the very top is a plain place, a rocky platform, whence the eye searches all that valley and views the great vale and the roads below, and Blencathra and Skiddaw rising beyond them, and the mountain tops of Helvellyn above the nearer crags, and Ullscarth over the moor. So that this was the safest place for refuge, and the most dangerous whoever should attack it that could be found : a stronghold seemingly impregnable before the days of gunshot, and still among the wonders of Lakeland.

Here it was, our story says, that Gartnaidh kept ward on the passes with his men, and held Thorstein in a prison from which there was little escape. But so long as Raineach was there, life was not bitter nor unbearable : for she was all the world to him now.

And yet there was little to give them pleasure in the horrible black rocks and roaring gill, and the loneliness and deathliness of all around. Gart-naidh came and went with his men, never leaving the place without a guard upon the gateway, so that none might go out or come in. And indeed, what with wild beasts and the terrible country round about, to say nothing of a time of war when every kind of evil-doer is abroad, there was little to tempt them forth so long as they had a roof over their heads, if it were no better than a pighull ; and a wall between them and the world, even though it were a prison-wall.

The summer sultriness thickened day upon day, until Blencathra was but a film of grey, hung like a cobweb in the sky : and the beck began to dwindle, and its roar died into a murmur beneath the bul-warks of the hold. Then followed the stillness and the heaviness that makes one weary in the hour before a storm bursts. But if the sky was threaten-ing and if the air was full of dread, in their hearts was a still greater unease while they waited evening after evening for the news that must by now be on its way to them—the fulfilment of Aluinn's sight-seeing and the sooth-saying of her mother.

One night the men came back and called for drink; and Raineach brought them what mead there was, strongest of strong waters. Gartnaidh drank and bid Thorstein out of his sight. The lad crept into one of the ruined chambers—low bields they were, like dog-kennels against the wall, in the lap, so to say, of that Castle-crag : and he lay there long, waiting for the thunder to begin. But all he heard was the sound of loud voices, and furious talking, and Raineach's shrill tongue scolding, begging, threatening; and at last a smothered scream, as if some evil had happened. His heart went quite cold, and he crept out to die with her. She was there beside him, sobbing and shuddering : but she put her hand upon his mouth, and drew him into the chamber.

" He has beaten me," she whispered : " and he will kill thee. He says the wolf-cub is a burden, now the wolves are slaughtered. And he will kill me too, if I stand in his way. He is wild. Oh, Thorstein, listen ! he is coming ! "

There were shuffling footsteps without : the giant, drunken with strong drink, was groping towards them in the darkness. His hand pressed the broken thatch of the shed where they lay, and the underside of it cracked away and dropped on them. But he could not find the door. After a while he growled and muttered, and sank into slumber.

" Thorstein," said she, " let us away while he sleeps. Oh save me, lad, and save thyself out of this den ! "

Then Thorstein, terrified as he was, tried to soothe her : and in a while the quietness gave them courage to look forth.

## CHAPTER XXV

### *HOW THEY FLED*

DAWN was at hand, and things began to loom through the blackness of mirk night. Gartnaidh snored on where he fell; but the gate-guards lay in their places, whether sleeping or waking the children could not know; and none could open the gate without stirring them.

Thorstein looked over the bulwarks and down into the gill. Black it was down yonder; and even the waterfall, into which he was used to throw stones for pastime, on the fell-side over against them, had dwindled so that the white of it hardly showed. Beneath him the rock went sheer down for a space; and underneath, he knew that there were tufts of heather and saplings growing out of the scree-side that sloped from the crag. He stole breathless to one of the chambers where some little store of bedding and apparel lay, and brought out a bundle of girdlethongs and such like, and began to tie them into a line. But they were scantly enough to loop round a big stone, and to reach thence to the wall edge and a very little way overboard. He went back for an armful of skins: but how to rip them up into thongs without a knife?

Then Raineach crept up to the giant, and loosed

his sword in the sheath : and as she rattled it, he gave a great groan : and she let go. But he sank into sleep again, and she drew it out. They cut the skins into strips, and knotted their line in haste, with trembling hands, and threw it over the wall.

Raineach sat on the edge, and clinging tight to the line, slid down hand under hand, fending herself off the crag with her feet, until they touched the rough scree-slope. Down came Thorstein, with the giant's sword thrust naked through his girdle behind. Her heart beat lest the line should break, or the stones come away from the wall-coping upon them both : but at last he stood beside her, and they stumbled down the long slide of ruin to the gill. There was just light enough for them to cross it without being carried down the stream ; and they scrambled up the other side on the grassy bank of the waterfall as steep as a hill-side can be, all under those terrible hanging crags, in the glimmering dawn and the thunder-mist.

Then there was a roar and a crash, and splinters of stone flew about them. They saw the giant's head over the bulwarks against the sky, and his long arms whirling as he took aim at them again. She screamed and they ran up-bank on hands and knees while the stones flew, and the curses and threats with them. But they never looked behind again until they were a good step out of the deepest of the ravine, and well up towards the moor, where the ground was not so dangerously steep ; none the worse yet except for cutting their shins on the scree, and tearing their faces in the blackthorn bushes.

They stopped for breath, and a last sight of their prison : but they stopped only a moment, for the gate was opened and folk were running after them in the grey mist across the tongue of land. So they plunged into the birches and the bogs, and crept through the underwood, and waded through the tottermoss, startling the hag-worms beneath and the wild fowl above, as they beat their way up and ahead, hoping only to be lost and out of sight.

Then they came to a high ridge, with piked rocks standing on it, from which they could see that their homeward course was plain, over a great swamp and a bleak tarn, and along the green mountains beyond it. But from their rock they could trace the giant not so far behind, making his way through the wood, which was harder for him to force than for the lithe light bodies that could slip between its boughs, and over its half-dried, cracking mire-holes in which his bulk and weight stuck and sank continually. And yet he went at it with main strength, swinging his club and hewing a passage.

Down from their peak they flitted, and up he came from the other side, shadowy against the lurid sunrise. With a shout he strode over the edge, taking great steps against the sky, while they were lost in the maze of oozy rills, too broad for them to jump, and too deep and too treacherous to wade. While they looked wildly for their crossings, he leapt the ditches and gained on them, until at last he whirled his club round his head, and it flew hurtling through the air. They fell flat in the mire, and it skimmed close over them. Then they struggled to their feet and ran neck and neck for Blea tarn. Thorstein plunged in, dragging her after him, and struck out for the other side, sorely weighed down by her head on his shoulder, and well-nigh choked by her grip round his neck ; for she was no swimmer, and gasped and struggled in the black water. He landed her, though, upon a shoal, and up the bank they fled, on firmer ground now, and with a clear way before them and treeless, over stones and grass, forward and upward to Ullscarth.

But a terrible roar came up from the tarn ; and they looked back, and saw the giant near the middle of it, fighting with the black water, and lashing it into foaming waves that circled and spread until all the mere was in a turmoil. And then his head went under : but he rose again, flapping and battling like a wounded heron. Then he sank again, and once more came to the surface, drifting like a log in an eddy. And then the water closed over him, black and calm, and the pattern of the mountain tops began to take shape where he had been. The children stood fixed to the spot. A stream of bubbles rose, and burst ; and the reflections joined again. Raineach turned suddenly on Thorstein and dealt him a blow that felled him to the ground : she burst into a passion of weeping, as she flung herself beside him. " Thou hast killed my father," she wailed : " I hate thee, I hate thee ! "

Thorstein was in no mood to say good or bad

to her, so utterly weary was he; least of all to make love-speeches. He lay awhile, and the tarn-water ran from him upon the grass.

"Listen, Raineach," he said at last, "I hear the shouts of the men that follow us afar."

"Oh lad," she cried, "dear lad, take me with thee."

So they climbed the ridge, and held by it on the farther side, hidden from their pursuers, and saw them no more.

But now the day had broken, a dismal day of thunder mist and gathering storm. The highest tops were lost, not in their homely cloud-caps, but fading away into black vapour; and through the rents in it the sun shot beams of coppery and swarthy sheen, down into the smoky dells and tumbling precipices, that seemed to ditch their moorland road on either hand. The long rise and fall of Ullscarth before them looked like a vast bridge in the air, and leading nowhither but into darkness. Far to the right, gaps in the gloom showed awful edges of mountain, rolling and plunging along the skyline, as wheels that moved, great toppling balls advancing slowly over hill and dale, wayward and unescapable. Nigher at hand were huge monsters, misshapen and grey and foul to see; many-headed things, with eyes and crests and spiny backs, crouching along the naked ground, among white and bleaching bones in the black soil. And when the children came nearer, hoping to slip by, for there was no other way, these things became great boulders, as it might be images of unknown dragons of dreamland, or they were weird tussocks of grass on black and embattled towers and pinnacles of crumbling peat, that took the shape of laidly worms and all the terrors of winter-night tales.

They won their way over the bridge in air, down through the silky green mosses and heatherless moor-grasses, to Greenup raise; for they dared not try the valleys on either hand in fear of losing the only way they knew, the safe and solitary ridge that must bring them southward and homeward. But the darkness deepened, and then came a flash and an instant crack and roar that sent them speeding upward in panic. Then the storm began, flash upon flash of blue light, terrifying and bewildering, as they scudded through the din and rattle of hail, blindly seeking shelter; and dashed into a nook of white shattered rocks, an island on the great heaving billow of moor. As they crushed themselves into the bield, some ugly beast with a snarl and white teeth pushed out, and fled past them into the storm. And there they cruddled, in shelter at last; and such was their weariness and the heaviness of the air, that they knew no more until they awoke wondering.

For the sky was violet-blue above them, and the sun was going down among torn flitters of cloud-wreck. All around, the mountains were hard-edged and dark purple, with streaks and stripes and slashes of dim white from the hail and sudden cold. The children crept out, shivering and tottering.

" Oh, Thorstein," sobbed the lass, " I can go no farther ; let us lie down and die here."

But he comforted her, and bade her lean on him, and led her up the moor, slowly and painfully toiling, until step by step they gained a rocky pike among white tables of stone and strange pillars and domes and curving hollows, like the icebergs they tell of in the far northern seas. And looking homeward in the twilight from that tower, they saw a deep dark valley below, and weary fells on the other side, and dells and mountain moors. But beyond, far beyond, a gleam of water and a rising shadow of mountain beside it, that wiped off the stars from the southern sky. Aye, and Thorstein greeted as he held the poor lass up to look at the strip of light in the distance. " It is my mere, it is our own mere, Raineach. I know it ! "

How they came down Langdale side in the darkness they could never tell. From ledge to ledge, among the hammers and knots of rock, clambering and groping for foothold and hand-hold, sliding sometimes down the screes and losing one another in the deep fern ; but still descending, even when they were swept down the mazes of the black gills and the torrent beds roaring from the rain-storm ; lightheaded with hunger, and reckless from fatigue, they reached the valley.

Guided by a red spot of firelight they came upon the huts of the poor folk who had harboured them on their outward journey ; and there they found food and a respite from their travelling ; and made

a ready tale how the men had gone to the war and
sent them home. For if they had let it be known
that Gartnaidh was dead, it was odds but the fell-
folk would have been rough and mishandled them.
But for pity's sake they were good, and made them
welcome, and wondered how they had come
through the storm unscathed. They housed them,
and fed them, as long as they would bide, and then
set them a good step on their way, until they struck
the track over Hawkshead moor and down
Rusland pool to the Leven.

As they came within sight of Leven firth and
the well-known hills, wooded softly and winsome
after the horrible ruggedness of the mountains,
Thorstein laughed and sang and shouted for joy,
and stepped briskly forward. " Come along, lass,"
he cried, " come along with thee ! Yonder is
Legbarrow, and the sands of Leven ; a bit more
and we shall see Greenodd. Home, lass, home !
Step out. Why, what ails thee, silly ? "

" Oh, Thorstein, I dare not. My heart is like
water within me, and my head works sore."

" Aye, poor thing, little tired thing. I'll help
thee along. See : yonder is our howe ; and the
smoke from Greenodd. See the bonny fields and
flocks in them ; and ah ! they have built a new
cottage by the ford, and sown a bit of the intake
on the fell. There's Greenodd, Raineach ; there
it is, our own house ! "

" Nay, Thorstein, I can go no further. My feet
are broken, and my knees are trembling. Oh, let
me be, and leave me."

"Why, lass, it is but a step. Well, then; well, then; bide here if thou must, and look for me back in a hop, skip and jump to lait thee."

She saw him trip off with no more farewell; and then she dragged herself up into a wild apple tree, and it began to grow dark; and she waited for him, sick at heart. Then the night fell, and still she waited for him.

## CHAPTER XXVI

### THE ARVALE FOR
### SWEIN BIORNSON

GRAND doings were at Greenodd house. There was a table set out before the door and drinking horns upon it, and a vat of ale in the porch. Rosy-cheeked lasses, in their feast-day kirtles and ker-chiefs, served all comers by way of a welcome and a foretaste of the supper. For this day was the Arvale made for Swein Biornson who had fallen at the battle of Brunanburg.

It was their custom to bid to the funeral feast all their neighbours and friends, not only that they might do honour to the dead, but also that they might bear witness to the incoming of his heirs according to law and the wonted order of kinship. This they called Arv-ale, which is as much as to say Inheritance-ale ; as they said Bride-ale for the wedding-feast. And still in these parts the name is given to cakes they make at funerals, which they call Arval-cakes.

Now when Thorstein came up to the door, guests were in the act of arriving ; namely, a good neighbour whom he knew for Master Asmund, whose land was Asmundar-lea, away over the back fell ; he had come now and then to feasts and meetings at Greenodd. He was finely dressed in a new kirtle and hose of the best homespun; he wore a broad felt hood, and leather riding-boots with bright spurs to them; and when he lit down from his horse, he stood in the porch with a seasonable sadness, and drank his ale to the good luck of the house, and hemmed, and sighed, and wiped his beard, and walked in.

With him was a bright little slip of a lass, who must be his daughter, for one could see that her nag was well groomed and well fed; and though she was covered from head to foot with a great hooded riding-cloak of dark blue and somewhat splashed with mud, such a merry grey eye looked out from the hood and such a dainty foot stood in Thorstein's hand as he helped her from the saddle— for he happened to be the nighest—that there was no doubt of it, who she was. She just put the horn to her lips, cast her eye round with a little grimace, and mimicking the grave gait of her father, stepped in after him.

Thorstein looked at the servant-lasses, but they were strange to him. He saw that a feast was forward, and guessed well enough the reason why: for the fell-folk had already heard tidings of a great defeat, and he knew his father had passed him, that night of evil luck, on the way to the battle. He could put two and two together now. And as he stood in the porch, glad to be home again, it came over him suddenly that this was no more his father's house, and that his three-years'-long desire was unfulfilled after all: and the tears came into his eyes.

Just then stood forth a couple of finely dressed
young men, returned to the porch after bestowing
neighbour Asmund and his daughter within.

"Now, my good fellow," said Orm roughly,
"no loitering here with the lasses and the ale. The
thrall's quarters are yonder."

"Hold hard," said Hundi. "This is none of
Asmund's folk. He is more like a wild lad from
the fells, with his long naked sword. Nay now, he
is a queer one. What is thine errand, friend?"

Thorstein said nothing. Words failed him.
To think his own brothers knew him no more!

But just then the mother came out, wet-eyed,
but bustling over her guests, and anxious that all
should be rightly seen to. Nay, never ask if she
mistook him, or bade him be gone.

Well, the guests had come and the supper was
ready. The hall was hung with its finest tapestries,
and the floor new strewn with fern. After a
fashion that was sometimes followed then-a-days,
men and women were paired off to eat together.
Unna sat in her own high-seat, with Asmund as
honoured guest beside her. On her left hand was
Raud her brother, who had taken land just across
the water at Roudsey. One place was empty, the
high-seat of the master of the house; but in all
others men and women sat according to their rank,
for the women's thwart-bench was not yet come
into fashion, but if for weddings. As it fell out,
Thorstein was given for his partner the young lass
Asmund's daughter, Asdis by name. Folk nodded
and patted the table with hard fingers when they

two sat down, as if to say " Welcome back ! " and as though they would add, " Well matched, lad and lass ! " For Asdis came out of her cloak like a butterfly from its shell ; and Thorstein, when his mother had bathed him and trimmed his hair and dressed him—and little else she did before supper-time from the moment she set eyes on him—why, then he was quite another lad, and they all said as much. Hundi was quite friendly, and Orm was civil enough ; though he whispered to Hundi, " Why couldn't the fellow have come to-morrow ? "

" Eh ? " said Hundi, bluntly. " Why to-morrow ? "

" Only that half is more than a third, thickhead."

Then Hundi went over to Thorstein and kissed him, and gave him a good slap on the back, saying " How about that whale, lad ? " At which they all laughed, for they knew the story well ; but sobered themselves of a sudden and fell to business, namely their supper. Asdis, the roguish lass, ate off Thorstein's plate and drank out of his cup, for at feasts when guests outnumbered the household goods, that was their way. And between the mouthfuls she chattered in a low voice, for it was not seemly to speak loud at a feast for the dead.

" So, neighbour Thorstein Sweinson, ye've been seeing the world ? "

" Aye."

" And maybe you've set eyes on a deal of grand folk, kings and queens and such like ? "

" Aye."

" You don't say so. Hark to him. Happen

you've been faring to Micklegarth, and aboon ? "

" Nay."

" What then ?  Not over seas ?  Well, maybe over the fells and far away ? "

" Aye."

" And clean forgotten thy mother tongue ;  or more like grown a peacock, that has never a word for such as us ? "

" Nay."

" I thought as much.  Tell me, neighbour, didst thou see a ragged lad in the porch this afternoon ? "

" Nay."

" Good.  Then I'll tell thee.  He was a scarecrow, he was.  Who'd have thought of a prince in disguise ? "

And so she went on teasing and bantering him, while he could not but spy at her round the corners of his eyes, so pretty she was in her low-cut kirtle and gold necklace on a white smooth neck, with the locks of her unbraided yellow hair brushing his sleeve, and the dimples in her little soft knuckles coming and going, as she handled and turned the cup before him.  She was so dainty that he was fairly abashed, and never knew how to answer her, and hardly dared touch the trencher with his rough paws.  There she was laughing softly, and joking in a whisper, with her apple-blossom chin over his shoulder ;  and folk staring at him too, till he was fit to sink under the table.  Then he drank up all the ale, and held out the cup for more, and drank that ;  and then he felt more blate than ever, and sat stock still, for fear he should do something foolish. For ale-drinking was strange to him; he got little stronger than milk on the fell, at the best of times.

When they had eaten, healths were drunk; a cup to Thor, and a cup to each of the gods. At each health they all rapped the tables and shouted. Then one stood up and hemmed and coughed— it was Master Asmund their neighbour; and he spoke in a loud sing-song voice:

"Friends all, and neighbours, here we are met together under this kindly roof-tree on a joyful errand—nay, what say I? Joyful is the day that brings the wanderer to his home" (at which they shouted, "Hear him, welcome Thorstein Swein-son!"). "And joyful it is to find a hearty welcome from our worthy hostess, even in the midst of her great sorrow" ("Well said," they cried all). "And right and meet it is to come together to cheer the widow and the orphan, and to speak a word of praise for him that is gone." ("Speak on!" they cried.) "Aye, friends and neighbours, he was a good man, was Swein Biornson. When I bethink me of the days he used to come home, ten and twelve winters it is and more, from summer-leading, before ever this new order of things began, when there was none of the nonsense that's talked nowadays about folk-right and king's law and the like: I say when I bethink me of our good neighbour that was, and him coming home by harvest time as regular as the swallows in spring, with a shipload of fine wares that had cost him

many a hard knock in the gathering, and many a
long cruise on strange coasts, and through stormy
seas : I can see him once again in his seat over
yonder, at the feast he used to give for his home-
coming and the harvest of the sea, and well I mind
his hearty voice; 'Take thy time, neighbour,
make thy choice,' he would say ; for he had a
gift in the heap for every guest, and a good word
with it. And when I look round on the land he
stubbed, bonny corn-riggs and lea land it is now,
and few of ye can call to mind as well as I the rough
spot this used to be, before ever he set to work
upon it ; when I come over the fell and look down
on this fine house he raised, fit up it is with every
comfort, and nothing awanting to suit his lady,
highborn as she may be, what with householding
gear and servants out-doors and in, dairy fit for a
king's daughter and byres of the best, and all the
stock so well managed—for there's a deal more
in managing, mind you, than some folk allow, that
are always blaming their luck for every beast they
lose, and every load of hay that they let rot in the
rain ; I say he was a grand man, and long will it
be or we see the like of him again. It is not his
friends only that say so, mind you ; they tell me
the very king of England himself offered our neighbour to make him a thane, and set him over the
country-side to take scat of the folk ; but ' Nay, '
says Swein Biornson as proud as a prince, ' Nor
thane of thine nor thrall of thine will I be,' says
he to the king. ' I am a free statesman, and a
good neighbour to all,' said he ; ' and ye kings may

L

lait your tools otherwheres.' That was a grand
speech, friends ; and many's the grand word we
have had from him over yonder at our meetings,
and many a time folk have been ruled by his rede.
For look you, friends, there was never a man of us
but kenned right well that Swein Biornson spoke
his mind, and every word came out of a good
heart, and honest ; though maybe we could not
all of us go as far as he did, in some matters. And
now," said Asmund, bringing his speech to end,
" He is gone, and we shall see him no more. Over
the fells in the great battle-play, hewing down his
foes as a lad haggs weeds with his wand, leaping
through the spears of the English and shouting to
the cowards who dared not follow him ; the kemp
and captain of the little band that backed him,
until the Saxons faltered and fled, so they tell the
tale that saw it. Aye, and if Owain and Constantine and Olaf the Dane had but found a handful
such as he, there would have been another tale to
tell of the doings at Brunanburg. But it pleased
the Allfather to send for him, and take him to
himself. Right glad we should have been to have
laid our neighbour in his own howe, to overlook
the lands he has won and the house he has planted ;
but afar on the Winheath he lies, and Odin has
spared him the sorrow of a straw-death. Let us
be glad, friends, and rejoice for him ; for the
deeds he has done in his life, and for the glory he
has gathered in his death. Drink with me this
cup to him ; drink to Swein Biornson."

Standing up, they drank in silence ; and in

silence they sat down again. Then Orm Sweinson, as being the eldest son of his father, stood
in his place to drink the Bragi-cup. It was their
custom at Arvales to leave the dead man's high-
seat empty until his health had been drunk, and
honoured with some fitting speech or vow made
by him who should be the chief heir to the name
of the dead ; and not until then might he sit in
the empty high-seat, and by that token take the
rule over the house of his father.

So Orm's cup was filled, and he rose and came
into the middle of the hall, and stood with one
foot on the stone curb of the hearth. " I drink,"
he cried aloud, " this cup to Bragi ; and I vow
hereby to do vengeance for the dead, and justice
to the living." Then they cried out that he had
vowed well ; could say no less and need say no
more ; and they made room for him to take his
place upon his father's seat, as master of the house
thenceforward.

Then far into the night they sat to drink, and
each man told his tale of him that was gone, or
sang a song in honour of him. But long before
they were done with their feast, Thorstein's eyes
were closed, for he was heavy with travelling, and
with the joy and sorrow of home-coming, and
maybe also with the strong ale he had drunk. So
he slept where he sat, long after Asdis, pouting
and vexed, had gone off to her chamber with the
rest of the women-kind.

Thus ended the first day of the Arvale for Swein
Biornson. And all the while, in the dark night,

Raineach clung to the branches of the wild apple tree by Crakeford, weary and hungry and sick at heart, and listening for Thorstein. And when she slept for very weariness, she dreamed that he was dragging her among proud strangers who scorned her; and then that he was saying, " Off, off, ugly paddock." And she awoke weeping, and listened for him, in the patter of the rain upon the drenched leaves in the dawning.

## CHAPTER XXVII

## *SWEIN BIORNSON'S HEIRS*

MORNING came and they were stirring. Thorstein found it hard to awake; but as he rubbed his eyes and shook himself, there came over him the thought of Raineach and how he had left her; and he was bitterly ashamed. He ran to his mother, and "Mother," said he, "I have been both knave and fool."

"What now, barn?" said she.

"Mother," said he, "I had a gold ring in my hand, and I dropped it in the ale vat."

"Never heed it, barn," said she; "thou wilt have gold rings enough, and that thou wilt see before to-day is done. And thy old one will land up when the ale is drunk."

"Mother," he said, "there was a young lass with me as I came along the road; and I left her hard by Crakeford; for she was weary, she said, and would come no farther."

"A lass, barn? What, thou art young to lead lasses up and down. But lads will be men nowadays, no sooner than they are out of swaddling clothes. And what sort of a lass may she be?"

"She's a good lass, mother, and a kind one to me; and I'd liefer by far lose ring or ring-finger."

"What then, lad? I'll say nay to nothing, now I have thee home; but be guided. Here we are all throng as throng can be, and folk to break their fast; and men-folk are aye fractious on the morrow of a feast until they be served. And there's the settlement to follow, and a gey work it will be to get through unless Orm be more reasonable than I fear. Let me send one of our men to lait thy lass, and bestow her in one of the thrall's cots until we get these guests off our hands; or if thy mind is to fetch her here upon us all, maybe Asdis Asmund's daughter will give her a share of her bed. That's a bonny lass, Thorstein."

"Nay, mother," answered he, stuttering, "I doubt Asdis will give us no thanks for thrusting a stranger upon her; and Raineach——"

"What?" said his mother, "is it an Irish woman?"

"Never mind what, mother, now; but I say she will be better suited elsewhere than here, until this turmoil is over, and then."

The first thing was their breakfast, which was a great meal with the North-folk then-a-days, and the set-out was well-nigh as big as at supper time. Next thing was the settlement, and division of the dead man's goods; to be done before the neighbours, fair and square and above-board; for in those days they had no lawyers and writings and such-like, either for the making of laws or for the conveying of property, and all was done by word of mouth and deed of hand in the presence of witnesses, whose testimony was the only token of the continuance of a custom or the assurance of ownership.

After question asked and answered about debts the dead man might owe, and after sundry to whom he had lent money or goods had repaid them in bags of silver or ells of cloth, they came to the division of the estate. It was their use for the widow to take one part in three, both of the land and goods. After some talk, they climbed the howe and parcelled out the whole landtake of Swein Biornson, both wild-wood and cleared land ; and coming down from the howe they all walked over the grounds as they had measured them out from above, beating the boundaries, and planting staves or stones from point to point along. And this side of the line, upbank towards Greenodd, was to be Unna's, and the other side was to be for the rest of the heirs.

Of furniture and movable things, ornaments and apparel and household gear, they carried out a third part and stood them in a heap in one of the sheds, until it should be settled where Unna would bestow herself and her goods. Then she chose out her third part of the thralls, both men and maids, and set them aside. And by that time the morning was spent, and the mid-day drinking was served to them in the disordered garth. But to the younger folk all this was a holiday-making, and it was merriment to see arks opened and goods shifted, and the thralls set out in a line and chosen : and to hear the maids say, " Oh, mistress, take me ! " and to one and another the mistress replying, " Nay, lass, I know thee too well."

So then they talked about what should be done as between the three lads ; until one said, " It has been done before, neighbours, and it is often a good custom, for the first-born to get house and land, and for the younger to take the movable goods. Now here we have three lads ; and if we set all that remains in three shares, namely house and land and farming-stock to one share ; and the ship and all that belongs to it, boats and boat-sheds, tools and tackle and such-like, to another share ; and lastly, if we reckon up silver and gold, apparel and furniture and such chattels to the third share ; then I say we shall not be far from a fair parting of the estate. And I say that if Orm Sweinson takes the house and farm, he will do well ; and if Hundi takes the ship and goes abroad, he is like to thrive ; and if Thorstein the child gets the money and movables, he will be well set up."

At this Orm boggled somewhat, for, said he, " An empty house is cold cheer." But Thorstein answered, " Why, brother, we can mend that. Give me and my goods house-room, and I will give thee the help of me and mine." And so said Unna, for she was loath to leave the old spot, and Orm knew right well what a manager she was. And so they settled it, without more ado, and went down to the field for a game of wrestling.

There they played until supper time, and Thorstein acquitted himself right well, though he was hardly fifteen years of age and far from full grown.

But his life on the fells had hardened him, so that Hundi Snail, as they called him because he was easy and fat, went down under the youngster; and even Orm was thrown twice out of thrice, at which he was vexed, though he said little. So to set matters right Unna bade them in to supper; and as they went up to supper said Asmund to Thorstein, " A word with thee, my lad."

" Say on, master," says he.

" Look you now," says Asmund. " Thou hast been these three winters away, and no doubt we shall hear of thy doings. But one thing I see, and that is, thou hast not lost thy time."

" Thank you kindly," says Thorstein.

" But," says Asmund, " take a word from one who knows. It is not all of us who have the trick, like thy poor father, of being soft to friends and sour only to foes; and even betwixt brothers things do not always fall as one would. Now, was it quite wise in thee to throw thy brother Orm, think'st thou, those two times? Was not once enough?

" What ! " said he, " I threw him fair."

" Ha ! ha ! " laughed Asmund. " Fair is foul in such matters. Riddle me that, lad. But when thou comest to know Orm a bit better, from serving him a month of two——"

" Serving him ? " cries Thorstein.

" Well, what else ? since he is master of the house, and a masterful man at any time. But when thou hast need of a friend and a friendly roof over thy head, take thy money-bags, if aught be left

in them, and hie thy ways over to Asmundarlea.
Say no more, my lad, but bear it in mind."

So they went to supper, and Asdis sat again by
Thorstein, daintier than ever, and not a bit put
out with him; and he was a deal more at his ease.
And while men drank after supper, said she,
"Bonny things, master wrestler, I spied among thy
goods; and a lucky lad is the getter of them."

"Aye," said he, "they are fine enough, I
suppose."

"Would it be asking over much to have a sight
of them once again before we go? There's a
stitch in some of thy hangings I would be glad
to learn."

So he brought an armful and cleared the table
where they sat, and she fingered the embroideries
and praised them, and praised him, until he had
given her a good half of them in spite of her nays.

"What," she said at last, "I'll see no more if
everything I touch is to be given me. But in one
of thy kists, I saw a fine draught-board. Shall we
have a game?"

"I doubt," said he, "I have forgotten how to
play."

"Oh," said she, clapping her hands, "then I'll
teach thee, master mountain bear; and that will
be fun, for it's dull for us poor lasses if you men do
nought but drink till bedtime and aboon."

So he found the draught-board and the carved
knaves, and they played fox and geese until he
learned something of the trick of it. Then she
said, "Nay, thou art fairly my master. I'll teach

no more. Let us play rightly as folk do, and stake
a trifle on a game or two."

Well, the end was she won a good bit more of
Thorstein's fineries, and carried a great heap off
to bed with her. And if she was pleased, so was
he, at finding any way to please so pretty and
dainty a creature.

## CHAPTER XXVIII

### WHITE ROSE AND RED

Now the third day of the feast had come, when the guests bethought them of going their ways homewards. Thorstein went out with Asdis to catch her nag for her, and to set her on the way with Asmund and his men. But when they got up to the fell-pasture where the horses were, thralls were cutting wood from the stubs in the coppice hard by. And just as Thorstein was laying hold of the nag, what should he see but a poor, thin, gaunt figure in rags, among the wood-cutters, carrying a huge load of sticks, and the red hair hanging down unkempt over her face. One of the men, in rough horseplay, as rude rascals do with a strange new fellow-servant, put out his foot, and let her trip over it, and tumble with the load and all. Then another went up to her and cursed her for a fool and gave her a kick. Thorstein flew at them, and it was right for one and left for t'other, and down they went, heels over head, one with a broken jaw and one with bloody nose. Thorstein picked up the lass, and would have kissed her, but she fought herself loose and struggled away.

" Raineach ! " he cried ; " Raineach ! "

She turned and looked at him in his finery. Then she looked at Asdis who had come up, staring.

Then she looked down at her tatters, and black, bare feet and fingers.

Asdis put her hand on Thorstein's shoulder. " Eh, what breaks ! " she giggled, and then burst into shrieks of laughter. Thorstein shook off her hand, and darted after the ragged lass, who fled through the wood.

" Oh, Raineach ! " he cried after her in her own language, " Raineach, my darling ! forgive me, forgive me ! Listen to me ; only hear me ! Stay, Raineach, only stay, and hear me ! "

Poor little thing, she was too weak and ill to run far ; and stopped at bay under a ridge of rock in the wood. But still she kept him off with her hands, while she wept and laughed and wept again.

Thorstein grovelled on the moss before her, and poured out his heartful of passionate words, blaming himself for knave and fool, and excusing himself by telling her what had passed, and how his mother had promised to have her well bestowed in a thrall's cot, out of the way of the stoore of the guests ; and how he could not come nigh her till they were gone ; and over and over again he said it, till he had no more to say. At last he lay quite still, sobbing bitterly.

" What's all this ? " shouted a rough voice through the wood. It was Orm. " Look here, young fellow, don't go knocking my thralls about ; I'll thank you to learn manners, if you mean to stay. And who is this ugly goblin, I'd like to know ? "

Thorstein was on his feet in a moment, and

Raineach in his arms as if they had never parted.

"She's my sister, kinsman; the child of my foster-father. And I give thee to know, that there's not a lass in the land to match her."

"One would think the giant had fostered thee, barn," said Orm, using the old byword, and laughing scornfully.

"Then beware of the giant's fosterling."

"Well, come and show thy mother what a prize thou hast got."

"Aye, that I will, and all the world," answered Thorstein, as she nestled to him, and clung to him, sobbing no more, but tall and straight and proud, in her rags and dirt.

And then he led her to Greenodd house, whence all the guests had gone away; and speaking in her tongue, told his mother who she was. And his mother answered him, and spoke to her words that she could hear, and that made her weep for gladness. And when she was washed and fed, and dressed in clothes from Thorstein's own store, simple things that Asdis had not cared to take, she sat by the fire while Thorstein told them, far into the night, the story of his wanderings and of her kindness to him.

As the story went on, Unna drew nearer to her the child, that wondered, and understood nought of the tale but what she guessed from their glances; until her head was on the good mother's lap, and from her eyes, half shut, the tears crept out, and through the great red mane, upon the kind hands that petted her.

When Thorstein had done, Hundi kissed him, and Orm came over out of the high-seat he was proud to keep, and held out his hand. " Kinsman," he said, " let bygones be bygones."

" Why," said Thorstein, holding his brother's hand, " what is there to forgive ? "

But Unna said, in the soft Erse tongue that came back to her like a dream of childhood, " Many a time have I prayed, whiles to the Allfather, and whiles to the White Christ, for a little lass, though I dared tell no soul else of the folly. And he has heard me, whoever it is hears poor folk's prayers. He has taken my man to himself, and he has sent me this bonny maid."

# CHAPTER XXIX

## RAINEACH AT GREENODD

IT was not all plain sailing, though the start was fair. They tell how, once upon a time, a lad brought home a wild kitling from the woods, and nursed it up among the house-cats by the hearth. So it was at Greenodd with Raineach.

With the best will in the world, she found it hard to learn their ways, and quite beyond her to follow them. At first there was the labour of a new speech to get. Thorstein had picked up her talk with ease ; but she could never frame her lips to the strange sounds, nor force her thoughts into the words of the Northfolk. She would be eager to chatter, and brimful of news, or wonderment, or recollection, or explanation ; helping herself out with gestures, and the forcefulness of her native manner, unlike the slow steadiness of the Northern delivery, and strange to them and disquieting. And in the midst of it all, a word wrongly spoken, and drolly misinterpreting her meaning, would set them all roaring with laughter. At which she would be vexed and sulk, for her people were grave and staid, though forceful and rapid in speech and gesture ; while the Northmen, slow of speech and drawling, were ready with rough jokes and childish fooling. So she took their laughter in bad part ;

and they took her glumping for the sign of a bad heart; and Thorstein had work enough to come between them all.

And then she could never learn the deft neatness of their household ways, their cleanliness in kitchen and dairy, and tidiness of table and chamber, and handy management of needle and shuttle and rock. If there were doubt in their counsels, mishap with beasts or men, or any grave trouble befalling, who but Raineach was run to for help; for she kept her head, while the other women-folk were shrieking and scurrying; and she was dry-eyed while they were weeping; or sober while they giggled like fools. But even for that they thought worse of her, as one who had not the feelings of other folk, and never laughed nor greeted when she ought, nor was shocked like a decent lass, nor disgusted like a dainty one.

And that bush of red hair was never dressed for long; and her kirtle was torn, and cobbled up coarsely, and her kerchief awry, and her work fouled with losing, and leaving in corners, and crumpling in hasty forgetfulness. And if sometimes she was the pride of them all, for her tall, slim strength, and her bright, bonny face with the proud high-set cheek and brent brow, and with the earnest friendliness that shone in her eyes; at other whiles she was dismal, and the light faded out of her, and she was no better than a draggle-tailed slut, they said. And then nothing healed her but a run with Thorstein on the fell, and un-maidenly scraffling among the beasts, or rough

M

pulling and hauling at the boat-sheds with Hundi and the ship-wrights. Unna would often say over to herself how much she owed the lass for Thorstein's sake, and how much she might do for the lass to bring her into shape; and so schooled herself to be good to her; but it was not always easy to keep back a sharp word, and a sharp word spoiled everything.

Thorstein too was a puzzle to them. Every indoor business he shirked, and cared only for herding and boating and the rough work of the farm. He had been so long on the fells that quiet life came amiss to him; and often by the fireside at nights, as that winter wore, he would fidget and worry until he found a call for turning out, so that even the shepherds bade him leave them in peace to look after their own job. Then he took to hunting, and they owned he was a famous hunter. He would fish in the firth, day and night and all weathers, as if he had a bear's warmth in him. They were glad of the fish he brought home; but it was irksome to have him bring in his dripping self along with it, to reek and simmer by the hearth, when all was redd up and snug for the evening. "Folk must do as folk do," said they behind his back; but when they said it to his face he looked ugly, and Unna dreaded a fight with Orm one of those days.

So the nights wore on to Yule; and then came a messenger from over the fell to bid the Greenodd folk to Asmundarlea for the feast-tide; and "Over and above that," said he, "my mistress Asdis bade thee in especial, Thorstein Sweinson, and charged thee to bring the young may, for she would fain know her, and make a sister of her."

When Raineach understood that this was the lass that had laughed at her, on that dreadful day which nobody ever named, she said flatly that she would not go. But Unna begged hard, and told her that the lass was good at heart, and meant all kindly, and that it would be a feather in her cap to win such a friend. So Raineach dared say no more, though she loathed the journey.

But Thorstein found her some right bonny fairings and tricked her out as never was ; and Raineach was child enough to be proud of her attire, and said in her heart she would be a match for them all. And they took her on a nag like any lady, and rode over the fell, and were received heartily ; and all went well at first.

Asdis was a handsome lass in her way ; less tall and strong than Raineach, but far more snod and neat and womanlike. Raineach at her best was a wild-wood goddess, and at her worst she was a grey-faced tatterling again ; but Asdis was always the same, blithe and bonny, well set up and well seen to. So that one would have thought there need be no strife between them.

But the very next day Asdis was at her tricks, and everyone but Thorstein aided and abetted her in showing off poor Raineach in little things, that bit and stung like midges on a wet midsummer eve. She would flatter till Raineach was led into simpering, and then they chuckled ; she would ask her advice about tapestry stitches, and Raineach, seeing no malice, would give grave counsels that a body might see were nought; she would mock her gait and manner of eating, and entice her to say the words she always said wrong; and folk would laugh, and even Thorstein laughed as one who couldn't help it. Then Asdis cast a sheep's eye at him, and as it were claimed him for her friend and ally, and Raineach was furious, and paled, and blushed, and wept, and sulked. Asdis did it all so cleverly, and was so pretty and innocent over it, that even Thorstein would take her part and bid Raineach not be a fool. She promised to amend, and was bitterly ashamed, and tried again; and so it went on until they were all glad to part and get home again. And Master Asmund at the farewell clapped Thorstein on the back and said, " Well, lad, we'll not forget, and we look to see thee when thou art tired of Greenodd and all thy folk." And so the lad was set up with himself, and vexed with Raineach, thinking that she had spoiled their sport, and was after all no better than a pettish child.

One day when Yule was well over, his mother called him aside and " Lad," she said, " I doubt I am wearying of these doings. It's not that I don't love the lass from my heart, and there's nothing I would not do for her. But its dreigh work putting up with her whimsies, and setting things to right after her. Never a stitch she sets, but I have to unpick it; never a pat of butter she turns, but I have to wash it; what, and she was stirring the cream this very day with a horn spoon when the rowan thival was there at hand. And she slaps the servant lasses if they so much as smile, and she has words with the men, aye, even with Orm himself. Why, he said to me this very day, Mother, said he, tell that young spitfire that I'll have no more of her sauce ; let her know who is master here, said he."

" Well, mother," said Thorstein, " Raineach is a good lass, and means well."

" Nay, never doubt it," said his mother. " But she does ill, and sets us all by the ears. It's grieved I am to say it, but I would be thankful if one she would hearken to gave her a word and got her to amend."

" You are hard on her, mother. You all said you'd take her for one of us, and make her at home. And it's nothing but tease and worry, till the poor child never knows whether she's on her head or her heels."

" Nay, Thorstein ; that's not a fair word to the mother that bore thee. Who brought her here ? Who fetched the wild cat into the house ? "

Then he was angry, and she was angry, and they had high words, and parted with little peace between them.

He went out to look for Raineach, and " Lass," he said, " what hast thou done to set them all against thee ? "

" I ? " said she. " Peace for shame, Thorstein ! "

" Nay," he answered, moodily. " It's truth.

Here's mother can stand it no more, and Orm fit to turn us out of the house."

"Well, then, I'll go for one. Thou canst stay if thou wilt."

"Raineach," he said, "hear reason."

"Little reason in you folk," she answered. "And thou, Thorstein, once I thought——" But she burst into weeping, and fled away.

Thorstein turned in again, angry with her, and more angry with his folk, and angry most of all with himself. As he sat and thought it out it seemed to him that this would blow over like other storms, and that Raineach would surely come back to supper. But supper-time came, and no Raineach.

"What's to do with the lass?" said Unna. "Well, hungry folk can't wait, and I'll keep a bite against she comes."

"Nay," said Orm, "sulky dogs go supperless."

But Thorstein was uneasy, for he had never before parted from her in anger. He left his porridge in the bowl and went out. It was starlight, and snowy, and he called her name. But the sound died away over the dim white fields; and he went forward calling for her, and into the fields and up to the ford.

He searched high and low, far into the night; and knocked at the thralls' cots to ask for her. At last one said, coming sleepily to the door, that he had seen her in the gloaming making her way to the fell through the bare woods. He knew it was the wild may by the glint of red in the boughs on the snow. Then Thorstein was terribly fleyed, and ran to seek the place where she had been seen. He found her track in the snow and followed it up, leaping with all his might, breathless, and stopping only now and again to call, and to listen for an answer. The late moon rose, and her traces were still there, the little holes where her feet had gone, and the blur where she had stumbled or rested.

It was long before he found her, plodding ahead up the fell, far beyond their bounds.

"Let me go," she cried, "to my own people. Let be, and forget Raineach."

"To thy people?" he said; "then I follow." And he tramped onwards by her side.

After a while she said, "They will kill thee. Go back."

"What do I care?" said he; and they went on.

Again she said, "Thorstein, thou art a fool."

"No news," said he.

Then it began to dawn; and they were far on the moor, and the mountains stood tall on the rosy sky. She sat down in the snow, and he sat beside her. Suddenly she put her hands before her face and burst out into wild laughing. "Fools we are both," she said. "Look at yon sky, and our own fells, white and still. And we with storm and blackness in our hearts. Oh Thorstein, wouldst thou truly go with me?"

"To the end of the world," said he.

"And beyond?"

He took her in his arms, and the sunrise

brightened upon them. Long they sat together in the glow, and forgot the night, and the blackness in their hearts, and all the evil of bygone days. They seemed to have grown old, now, and wise. What silly children they had been, once.

It was late in the afternoon when they came into Greenodd hall, where all went on as ever : but the two were changed, and saw the spot as in a dream.

" Mother," said he, " I have brought her back. Let us rest here awhile : and give us thy blessing. We'll trouble the house no more : give us time, and we'll away to a spot of our own."

" Children," said Unna, " what game is this ? "

" I am a man now, mother," said he. " I can fend for myself, with her to help me. Never say nay : we have it all planned, and ask nothing but good-will."

" Good-will, my son, you have : aye, the best. But, barn, hear reason. You are young yet, and little you know of life. Bide awhile ; take your time. Who but guessed what it was coming to ? But Thorstein lad, if thou love thy lass, be guided. There's house to build, lad, and gear to get. Will you live in the wood, and eat mast like swine, with a starving brood of piglings running naked in the mire ? A man, lad, takes a man's rede : and a woman, lass, must grow womanly. Is it all done in a night ? "

## CHAPTER XXX

## THORSTEIN GOES ABROAD

YOUNG they were, but no fools. They kept their promise. Raineach was a new creature, anxious to please and amenable to guidance; willing to learn all that Thorstein's wife should know. He on his part acknowledged that there was a deal to do before he could set up house : and when Hundi sometimes joked him about his castle that was to have been on the shore of his mere, he would take it quite soberly, and reply, "Aye lad, I was a bit before-hand : but wait until I have got my gear together, and then."

"Better come for a trip with me this season, and see what skill we make at cheaping. With thy goods on my ship, thou and I might do a conny bit of trade, and see the world : maybe we'd light on luck, and come back able men."

Now it was a saying among these people "Homely wit has homebred barn " : and no lad was thought much of until he had been awhile abroad. There was none but Raineach that had a word against it ; and she was overborne the easier because she had made up her mind to be good, and think of her own wishes last.

So Thorstein busied himself in cleaning all the skins he had got that winter, and added a good few to his stock : and he packed up everything he could lay hands on, if only it would turn him a penny, or barter off against goods that would be useful to him in his housekeeping. And at last they bade farewell to all, and taking the shipcarles who had been used to voyage with Swein, they started merrily on a fine spring day, down the Leven, and stood over the sea for Ireland.

At that time there was an unwonted peace through the coasts of England and all round about. These were the last few years of king Athelstan's life, when he had brought his neighbours under him, or won their good will. He reigned in great glory and honour, and his realm prospered : his strong hand, or the fear of it, kept all the lesser kings and earls of the North in quiet. Folk were glad of a breathing-space after an age of struggles and the great fight at Brunanburg ; and even across the sea there was a lull, so to say, in the turmoil of the nations. The age of the vikings was over, and it was now the turn of cooler heads and wiser counsels to set to rights the new order of things, and to establish the kingdoms and governments which had arisen out of the disorder and wreck of the old world.

By these days the Northmen had left being nought but rovers and robbers : they had become settlers and traders and rulers of realms on the seaboard of all the northern lands. And not only in the North ; for scarce a spot was there between Greenland and Constantinople where they or their children were not found, like bees in a garden, at once gathering honey for themselves, and sowing for others the seeds of new life and strength; the busiest and brightest of all the kindreds of the age.

But the Northern lands were their homes. On salt shores, where farming alone could never thrive; on bleak headlands among the seamews' nests; on lone islands veiled in the mist or girdled with the surf—homes where any but a race of sailors would have hungered slowly to death, or pined into dismal savagery—there they bred and multiplied, and sang through the winter, and strove through the summer; their wit and wisdom and valour putting to shame (though little they knew it) the follies and the vices and the idleness of the South. It were long to reckon up all that we owe them, in thought and speech, in law and custom, in arts and crafts; for without books, they made themselves learned; without schools, they became artists; without examples, they perfected laws; and without bigotry, they found freedom. A wonderful people, and greatly to be gloried in, even yet, by their inheritors; still more by their own children in the day of their strength. For a thousand years ago it might well be said wherever a Northman's keel strake strand there he found his kin to hand; be it west-over-sea from old Norway, in Britain or Ireland and the isles thereabout; or in Greenland or Iceland; or the Baltic coasts, and thenceaway to the Atlantic, from Finmark and Denmark to Holland and Valland; everywhere the Northman's tongue was heard and the Northman's hand feared.

It was no wonder then, if lads of the breed, born in this corner of no man's land, and nourished up among wild folk and woodland swine, should long eagerly to see the ways of the world and the dwellings and the doings of their kindred far and wide. Over and above the need to eke out the scanty gift of the earth by sea-going trade, there was the same spell that had beckoned them up the Crake, as boys—curiosity, and the love of adventure —hailing them now from over sea, and waving afar off who knows what glittering thing, to which reach out they must, whether they would or no. " Homely wit has home-bred barn "—aye, indeed, if his overword is always " Elsewhere, "and his day always " To-morrow."

So it was in the spring of the year, nine hundred winters, thirty and eight, since our Lord was born, the lads departed and came into Dublin Bay. And when they were landed, officers of the king stayed them to know their errand and whence they came. When they said they were chapmen, they were brought to the palace ; for the king's folk had the right to be first buyers, and to fix the price of wares.

At the gate who should spy them but Olaf Guthferthson himself. He asked the name of the bonny boys, and they told him their names and their father's name, and that they were from Hougun way.

" What," said he, " are you the sons of that brave Swein from those parts who fell at Brunan-burg ? Ah ! " said he, " if we had found but a few more such men, it's not in Dublin I'd be sitting

now, but holding my court in London town."
And when he knew for certain that they were the
sons of Swein Biornson the kemp, as he called him,
he brought them in to the queen, and bade her treat
them well, for they were the sons of a better man
than any of his.

So for a day or two they had famous entertainment, and thought themselves made men. But
they soon saw ugly looks among the house-carles
of Olaf : and one of their folk bade them beware
of a shrewd turn ; " for these Danes," said he,
" there's no trusting ; and stranger's praise is the
surest doom."

So they came before the queen and told her how
their business pressed, for that they had far to go :
and then she bade them farewell, but not willingly
as it seemed ; and a fine gift she gave them. And
as they scudded out of Dublin Bay, they thanked
their luck, and cursed all king's houses for downright wolf-traps.

Then, for the wind was in the South, they went
up and cruised about the Irish Sea to the Isle of
Man, and the great bights of Galloway. There
they met many of their own people who guested
them in one place and another, and gave them good
speed : but little trade they did, for their wares
were such as all men had in plenty. They sailed
from Galloway up the firth of Clyde, and by the
Isles of the Welsh, to Alclyde, which was also called
Dun-breton, where was the chief city of king
Domhnall : and there Thorstein was somewhat
shy of being known lest a grudge might be owing

him for his escape and for the death of Gartnaidh. But nobody seemed in those parts to know or care for old stories of wild fell-folk. He asked news of the queen, hoping to hear that his friend Aluinn was by now wedded to Domhnall and advanced to be lady of the land. But folk laughed and wagged their heads, and gave him to understand that there might be a dozen queens up and down for aught they know ; and he asked no more, for pity of the poor beauty away in the Cumberland fells, who had put her trust in the gay raking spark. He said a deal to Hundi, out of the fullness of his heart : what a shame it was that men should be light of love, and how he would like to see the blood-eagle carved on Domhnall's back. To which Hundi Snail answered lazily that he talked like a great guff : and Thorstein was near coming to blows with him.

When they came out of the firth of Clyde they rounded the Mull of Cantire and sailed to the Hebrides, and everywhere they found Northmen and friends settled, and an open market. So then they came to the mainland again, in Sutherland, and rounded Cape Hwarf, and so to the Orkneys.

At this time Turf-Einar the earl was dead, and his sons Arnkel and Erlend and Thorfin Skull-cleaver had the power. Thorfin's wife was Grelaug, the daughter of earl Duncan at Duncansby in Caithness, over the Pentland firth : and Grelaug's mother was Groa the daughter of Thorstein the Red. Thus there was even some far-away kinship between her and the lads ; and when this was brought forward they were taken as the

queen's guests, and they got protection for themselves and their men, and a good market for their
wares. And as the season was now far spent, and
the Northern seas are stormy when the winter
comes on, they asked that they might sit there in
Orkney until the bad weather was over, and offered
themselves to Thorfin to serve him. How they
wrought for him at ship-smithying, and fought for
him in raids on the Scots and on rough neighbours,
and how they saw many a roof burnt and many a
limb lopped, and how they hunted and drank and
quarrelled and escaped—all this is not in the story :
but no doubt they saw life as it was lived, both the
good and the ill of it, and hardened into sturdy
lads, fit for the give and take of the world they
dwelt in.

When spring was come they took their leave of
the Orkney folk, and sailed for Iceland : for they
had a great mind to see what was to be seen, and to
visit all the homes of their kindred, and never come
back until they could give a good account of their
voyage.

Now Grelaug of Orkney had a cousin out there,
the daughter of her mother's brother, Olaf Feilan.
The cousin was named Thora, and she was wedded
to Thorstein Codbiter, the son of Thorolf Mostrbeard, who built the great temple at Thorsness and
was a powerful chief among the Icelanders. So
Grelaug gave the lads a message to Thorstein
Codbiter and a token to her cousin Thora, nothing
doubting that it would get them a good welcome.

When they came to Iceland they asked their way

to Holyfell, the homestead near the temple. It was easy to find, for every one knew the name and fame of it : and in a few days they came there, sailing westward and northward round the coast and in Breidifiord : but they learned that Thorstein Codbiter was dead, drowned in fishing a twelve-month ago come harvest-time. Thora was still there, keeping house for her child Thorgrim ; and her brother Thord Gellir was a great man in the country-side. So the lads were in no lack of friends here as well as heretofore, and made hay while the sun shone.

Their goods were loaded on Thora's beasts, and brought up to her house. Thorstein Swart, who kept the temple, and stood as Godi until Thorgrim the child should grow old enough to take the priesthood of his father, he fixed the prices, according to custom ; and then our lads were free to go about and trade with their neighbours. They sold their wares to such as wanted them ; and those that would not have them at the price fixed, had them not at all.

There was much for a stranger to see in Iceland. At Thor's-ness there was the new temple, and its high-seats adorned with the old carved pillars that came from Norway, and that showed the way to Thorolf Mostrbeard, when first he came off that coast and threw them overboard to drift ashore. And there was the inner house of the temple, rounded like the choir of a church, with the altar-stall, and the great ring lying upon it by which all oaths were sworn, and the blood-bowl and sprink-

ling-rod for the sacrifices, and the images of Thor
and the gods standing round about.

After they had done their business, the lads went
with a party of their friends from Holyfell, riding
to the Iceland Althing ; and they saw the wonderful
valley with the precipices around and the deep rifts
that seam it, and the throngs that come together
year by year into the midst of that waste and
terrible wilderness of frost and fire.

But when they were safe returned and had taken
leave of Thora, they made ready for their voyage to
Norway : for they had a mind to see the old home
of their kin, and to come before king Hakon the
good, the fosterling of Athelstan of England. So
in the summer, when the days were long and seas
were fair, they sailed east, and came safely to
Throndheim.

N

## CHAPTER XXXI

## KING HAKON THE GOOD

IN Throndheim this summer sat the young king Hakon, newly come from the West country where he had wintered. He had been well received by the Throndheimers, for he promised them to get back all those rights which his father Harald Fairhair had taken away threescore winters ago : and over and above that he was a handsome lad and well spoken, every inch a king. Earl Sigurd of Ladir, the lord of the Throndheim countryside, was his great friend, and managed matters for him ; so that he came peaceably into the power, when his brother Eric Bloodaxe was once driven out, and away to England. " He was the blithest of all men, and the sweetest spoken and the kindest," say the stories : " and he was a very wise man, and set forth the laws of the people with the help of their wisest men; and in his time there was good peace amidst bonders and chapmen, so that none did hurt to other, nor to other's wealth, and plenteous were the season's both by land and sea."

So when our lads came over the sea straight from Iceland to Throndheim, they found king Hakon there, and went before him. He was big and strong, and very fair to look on, with long curling hair : and he was only of the age of sixteen winters, being a little older than Thorstein Sweinson and somewhat younger than Hundi.

He asked them many things of their voyage, and where they came from, and whither bound. And when they had told all their story and said they meant to go to England, and maybe to see London town, " Then," said he, " you will go to my home : for it was but last year that I came thence : and ever since I can remember anything I have been bred up there. I reckon it the best of all places, and would gladly live and die there, for the sake of king Athelstan my foster-father."

" King," said earl Sigurd, " that is bad hearing for us Throndheimers, and for all thy people of Norway."

" Nay, good friend," answered Hakon, " thou art hasty. For my mind was to say that I would fain be in England if I were not called hither by the best friends I have."

King Hakon bade the lads to supper in his hall ; and afterwards, when they were beginning to drink their cups to Thor and the gods, came a page to Hundi and Thorstein where they sat, and said, " Guests, if you have drunk enough, there is one would speak to you without."

So they followed him, and came into an orchard ; and under the apple trees they found the young king walking alone in the sunset.

" Welcome, friends," said he. " I owe you thanks."

" Thanks, king ? " said they.

" Aye : for maybe you had rather sit at table with

earls and famous men, drinking to the gods, than walk here with such as me ? "

They said that they were glad to walk with him, and thought it no loss to leave their drinking. " Hush," said he, " say nothing over loud ; for here in Norway folk must do as folk do. Maybe where you come from, the gods are honoured with drinking after supper, and with sacrifices at the Thing, and so forth ? "

They said it was so, among most : " But," said Thorstein, " though I know not if thou, king, wilt take it in good part, many of us are no great sticklers for the old faith, and some of us—"

" What ? " said the young king eagerly, but in a whisper, and looking round to see that none were by. " What, lad ? "

" I was but saying that some of us think maybe he they call White Christ is a stronger god after all than old Redbeard and the rest of them."

" And thou ? " said Hakon, looking earnestly at him.

" King," said Thorstein, " my father was a prime-signed man, and often has he told us the story of King Athelstan and his priest, and the good words they gave him, and how his own mind was one day to forsake the sacrifices. But it was not easy to be open about it, and then he died in battle."

The young king looked at him sorrowfully, and thought awhile. " It was not easy to be open about it," said he, "—and he died in battle. Where, think you, is he now ? "

"Nay, king, who can tell? He was a good neighbour, and gave every one his due, and died like a brave man."

"Ah, but," said Hakon, leaning back against the tree, "I have heard from a book they have in England, Whoso denieth me before men, him will I deny. That was what the Christ said. Oh lads, it is an awful word. It comes to me in the night as I lie awake : and then I sleep and seem to hear one saying to me, Hakon, I died for thee : what wilt thou do for me in all this realm of Norway that I have given thee? And then I have spoken to earl Sigurd, and he was angry with me, and bade me hold my peace, or lose everything. Oh, it is hard to be open about it, and yet—"

"King," said Thorstein, "I am but a youngster, and I have never heard sayings spoken out of books, nor even talked with a mass-priest. But I have a dear friend, and she had a cross that she prayed to : and one day she sold the cross for my sake when I was in danger. And when I asked her how she would pray, seeing she had no cross to pray to, she said that there was an old man whom she had seen after she had sold it, who bade her take comfort, for, said he, the God of the Christians, they call him the Lord, looketh at the heart. These were the words."

"Aye," said Hakon, "that is in the book."

"Is it?" said Thorstein. "Well, king, and if thy heart is with that Lord, is not all right?"

The lad Hakon took the lad Thorstein in his arms, and kissed his cheek. "Brother," he said,

" I brought you lads here to preach to you, and you have preached to me a better word than any since I was taken away from home to be a stranger among my own people, and an outcast from all kindly Christian men among the heathen. You have preached to me ; will you pray with me ? "

They understood nothing of what he said : but he knelt in the twilight on the grass, hidden among the orchard trees, while the shouting of the Bragi-cup was heard from the windows of the hall. They knelt beside him, and he said in a low voice, and as if sobbing, the Lord's Prayer.

Then he stood up radiant and joyful. "Brothers," he said, " stay by me here, and help me. I will give you all your heart can wish, only stay and help me in this terrible loneliness. We together will win the realm for the Christ ; or, if we must, die like the blessed saints and martyrs, and go to be with him in heaven."

Thorstein looked at the beautiful face, aglow with earnestness.

" King," he said, " I will slay thy foes for thee, and spend my heart's blood for thee. And I will take thy faith, and break Thor down from the temple yonder, if thou wilt."

" Hush, dear lad," said Hakon, suddenly be-thinking himself, and looking round with the old fear : " Hush, not yet. Oh, it is hard to know what to do. And there is no one to tell me. We must be gentle with them, and win them one by one : we must speak to them the words of life, and pray for them, and teach them."

Thorstein shook his head. " I could fight them, or some of them," said he. " But as to words of life, king, if they be the teaching of priests, I know nothing, for I am not even prime-signed."

" Ah, I forgot," said Hakon. " I am hasty. But you will not betray me. I thank you for your good will, and I love you for your good words : but it is other help I need. You are going to England, lucky lads. Do an errand for me."

They said they would do anything for him.

" Then go to Bishop Aelfheah at Winchester ; and tell him that his son Hakon remembers his teaching, and that he has sent two brothers of his to be christened. Take this token " (and he gave them a little cross which he drew out from his bosom) " and he will receive you. And then, if your mind is to come hither again, think of me and the work I have to do. Again and again I thank you. Come to-morrow ; but not a word to any soul of our speech together, if you love me."

They went to their quarters for the night, and though they saw the king again it was only when others were by. In a few days came some of the king's men with a rare gift for them, and a message bidding them take the fair wind before it fell. So they made ready and sailed out of Thrond-heim firth, and down the coast : and when they had coasted Norway they stood out West over sea and sailed for England.

## CHAPTER XXXII

## AT LONDON

AT last they were come to Grimsby at the mouth of
the Humber, and thence the way is plain, what with
river and what with road, to York, and over the
Keel into Cumberland, and so home. And indeed
the lads had a thought to lay up their ship and take
the journey forth and back to see how their folk
were getting on, and Thorstein especially to ask after
Raineach. But for three reasons they determined
to withhold themselves : first that they had resolved
to sail all round Britain and never go home until
they could tell their tale : and next that king Eric
Bloodaxe, the new king of York, who kept the
place under king Athelstan, was no friend to
Hakon, and awful tales were told about his queen,
Gunnhild the witch, so that they had no desire to
put themselves in his power : and last, that they
could not for shame forego their errand upon
which Hakon had sent them.

So they sailed round the coast until they came to
the Thames, and up to London. Off Billingsgate
they were stopped by the boats of the officers, who
brought them before the port-reeve : and when
they had told him their names and business, and
paid toll in four silver pennies, they were free to
dwell there. As it was now late in the year they

sought a lodging in the house of a Northman whom they met : and in order that they might buy and sell, and go freely among the Londoners, he brought them to a priest at the door of a church, who made upon them the sign of the cross, so that they should be prime-signed men, until they might find bishop Aelfheah and get christening at his hands.

At Yule was the Witan held at Westminster, and earls and thanes and bishops flocked together ; and among them the man they sought. Then they had their desire and did their errand to him, giving him the token of the cross and the message of the young king. The bishop wept over the tale, for joy that Hakon still bore in mind his teaching, and for sorrow that he should be out there alone among the heathen. " And yet," said he, " is it not written, Behold, I send you forth as lambs among wolves ? May the Lord grant his young child the wisdom of the serpent and the harmlessness of the dove, and in due time give him to see of the travail of his soul."

Then the lads asked that they might be christened and the bishop gave them in charge to one of his priests, who taught them as much as it was needful to know : and afterwards they were baptised. But when they spoke of going back to Norway, he smiled and said, " It is other help than yours that Hakon needs. You have done well in bringing this message, and no better news could be brought. As for his heart's desire, I take you two as the firstfruits of it. Do you depart in peace, to be shining lights in your own land. Without doubt when

Hakon is established in his kingdom he will send for priests fitted to teach his people, and never fear but there will be labourers for the harvest."

And here we may say that old stories tell how the bishop died some seven years after this, and was worshipped as a prophet and a saint. But the young king spoke first to one and then to another of his own friends and those about him in Norway, and without any other help of man, won them over to the Christian faith : and when many were thus converted he ventured to send for priests, and to hold open worship. But he was overborne by the common people, who would have nothing to do with the new doctrines. So for many a long year it was a struggle between them ; and every man that the king won over he counted gain ; and every time the Throndheimers forced king Hakon to come to their sacrifices and share their feasts they reckoned it gain to their side, even if they had done no more than make him smell the steam of the horse-flesh boiling in Thor's kettle. But for such backsliding as this the king blamed himself in secret, and went on in life-long fear of the doom of a castaway ; hoping from year to year that things would turn out so that he might lay aside his crown, and become a monk, and end his days in penitence. But his rule was so good that his people would not let him go ; and yet he still found it hard to be open about it, and at last died in battle, and was buried by the heathen with a great burial as if he had been one of them.

Now when the spring was come, Hundi and

Thorstein took their leave, and sailed out of the Thames and round the South coast, calling as they went at one port and another by the way, and always increasing their store ; until they came at last to Bristol, which was the great slave-market for the Irish trade in those days, and a thriving city. And thence they sailed down the Severn to those settlements of Northmen at Tenby and Milford and Haverford ; and so up the coast of Bretland, as they then called Wales, in whose firths, as in those of Morecambe and Solway, many a viking had refuged, betwixt Lund-ey and Orm's Head. From Orm's Head it was but a short passage to the bay of Morecambe : and by now they were wearied of seafaring, and longed for home.

And as they sailed briskly by the shores of Amounderness over the tossing green waves, Thorstein felt himself already in the arms of his lass ; and the spray from the bows where he sat, with half shut eyes, seemed like her hair blown about his face. At last the Black Comb rose over the sea-line higher and higher, and then the green woods, and then the yellow sands. There were Walney and the little islands, there were the cliffs of Alding-ham, there was the bonny Leven between its dear old hills.

" Eh, mother and Orm and all, its right good to be home again : " says Thorstein heartily ; " but where is—she ? "

Orm turned on his heel and went out.   Unna kissed Thorstein.   There were tears in her eyes.

## CHAPTER XXXIII

## THORSTEIN'S WELCOME

SPILT milk, they said. His mother assured him of it. Orm nodded aye, it was so ; and the thralls, men and maids, cried " What, master Thorstein is bad to suit : there's mays in plenty and bonny ones too, for a well-favoured young man like thee to light on."

Raineach had run away, and Orm, the good brother, had followed to fetch her back. He had tracked her with difficulty to the shipstrand near Ulfar's town. There he had seen her aboard a merchant ship, and there he had spoken to her, and she had laughed and waved her hands. And that very night a storm had come, and the ship had gone down with all aboard : not a doubt of it there was ; he could ask any one about the great storm two winters ago come haytime; and as for this ship, why folk at Rampside were still using the wreckage of her for fire-elding, or were doing so in winter. And the worst of it was that the finest of Thorstein's clothes and jewels, the things he had saved and left under Raineach's charge against the wedding, were all awanting, to the amount that a body might bundle up and carry off without other hands or help.

Again the mother said " She bade me fare-

well : " and the servants said " We spied her
start : " and Orm said " I called to her on board,
and she would not come back : " and they all
swore to the storm and the shipwreck as matters of
common knowledge.

" Humph," said Hundi Snail, " I didn't think
she'd have done it."

Thorstein was quite beaten down, and had
nothing to say. He went to Rampside, and saw
folk burning bits of the wreck that ran upon their
sands two years ago last haytime. They remembered it well, and how the ship folk yelled,
and what a crowd of corpses drifted ashore next
morning ; and oh aye, there was a lass with red hair
among them, no doubt : aye, bonny lasses and all.

" She's gone, sure enough, poor thing," said
Hundi : " but I don't understand it, somehow."

" Nor I," said Unna.

" Maybe," said Orm, " she had some notion of
meeting with Thorstein. She was always having
inklings of one thing and another, what with
dreams, what with fancies. And maybe she was
taking the gear to make her wedding with him, for
she seemed a bit nicked in the head. I wouldn't
call it stealing : what's mine is thine, the saying is."

" It's kind of thee, Orm, to speak up for her,"
said Thorstein : " above all, when I think she
didn't suit thee over well."

" Humph," said Hundi, " very kind of Orm."

When the seafarers' tale was told, and all their
goods shown, who but Hundi and Thorstein were
the pride of the place ? Folk came from far and

near and they said that it was none but their own
lads would go up and down the round world,
starting as youngsters with nought to speak of, and
landing home great strapping men who had supped
with kings and fought with earls—

" And courted the kings' daughters, and kissed
the earls' sisters," added a saucy voice.

" And brought home a shipload that would be
worth I reckon, about twice their father's stock,
beasts, thralls, and all."

" Well, father, we always said Thorstein Sweinson was a good lad and would turn out well." For
here was mistress Asdis Asmund's daughter of
Asmundarlea over the fell, as blithe as ever, and
bonnier, if that could be : anyway more womanly
grown, with a little motherly manner towards
Thorstein, as if she were very sorry for him—least
said soonest mended ; but she would make him
forget it after a while, and then. There was
nobody but was thankful to her : for they had
been dreading the day of his return and fearing how
he would take it. But Asdis was that clever, she
twisted them all round her fingers, and him in
particular, as wankle as a wet sark.

If Thorstein was moody and dismal, and he was
that, Hundi was jolly enough for both. To be
home again after a three years' voyage, and to be
made much of wherever he went, and to be master
of his half share in that rich cargo, let alone the ship
and boat-stock, all this made him welcome at every
neighbour's. As to his christening, they said he
could suit himself ; it seemed that it meant money

anyhow. And so it was no surprise when Hundi
begged his brothers to don their best clothes
and come with him awooing : nor when, after
the handfasting, he took land up the Crake,
and began to build him a house against the
wedding.

Thorstein was glad of the job, and worked right
hard for Hundi : and before Yule they had the
rearing-supper, and at Yule the wedding-feast ;
and started housekeeping merrily, with a full
larder and the best of good will from all. Thorstein went to live with them as foreman of the farm,
and there was a deal to do this winter, clearing land
and getting ready a thwaite for tilling. In the
spring Hundi meant to buy beasts, and pasture them
in the fell ; and meanwhile he had plenty to
live on.

Halldora Mani's daughter was the name of the
bride. She was a right good sort ; and Hundi was
that fond of her, and she of him, that Thorstein
could not but laugh, many's the time, as they three
sat together by the new hearth of nights. But if he
laughed, he would fetch a deep sigh, and then take a
turn up and down the floor : and Halldora would
get off the knees of her good-man and go to
Thorstein and bid him pluck up heart : and she
would take his arm and walk up and down a bit
with him. Then Hundi calls out from the hearth,
laughing, " Now, mistress, no carryings on with
my brother : it's me is thy man ! "

" Never fear," she answers coming back to him.
" The poor boy is sore at heart. And pity it is,

when the finest lass in the countryside would take him at the first word."

"What ? Asdis ? "

"Aye would she. Many's the time she has told me that she meant to get him, too. And I am sure there is no cleverer, nor bonnier, nor better bred. He might do a deal worse."

## CHAPTER XXXIV

## THE WOOING OF ASDIS

WHO knows what plots and plans were laid, and all with the best intentions ? The upshot of it was, one fine day appears Asdis herself, with men and maids, come to visit her dear friend Halldora in the new house. For three days it was " O Thorstein, how well you boys have managed ! what a fine house ! what bonny gear ! what a sweet spot ! " and so forth. And everything was Thorstein's doing, as if he had built the fells and rigged the very sky overhead.

" Heigho ! " she sighed, when Hundi and Halldora had left them alone, " it's bad to be illfavoured."

" Who's illfavoured ? " said Thorstein.

" Not Halldora, in her own house at home : and with a man of her own fit to kiss the ground she steps on."

" I warrant Hundi is a lucky fellow : but the mistress of Asmundarlea must be ill to suit if she waits a day longer than she likes."

" That's your London talk, Thorstein : thou'st gitten o'er fine for us hereaway."

" Never say so. Nay, Asdis : there's not an earl of the Northmen nor an English thane would be o'er fine for thee."

She rewarded him with a very sweet smile.

"What, we are old friends, lass, are we not?"

"Aye, neighbour Thorstein," and she gave him another smile and a blush.

"And I always spoke well of thee, even to her—to her that's gone."

"Nay, was it so? Poor lass, she's gone. Often have I wished I had managed to make friends with her: it was my fault."

"What was thy fault? That you were not friends? Nay Asdis: it was thou that was good to her, but she, poor thing, she couldn't understand."

"Ah, Thorstein, if there's goodness anywhere it's in thee. And well I know that after her the rest of us are nought."

"My dear, it's years she's gone; and it's months I have greeted for her; and now my heart is like a stone."

"Poor lad."

Her voice was like the cooing of doves in the wood, and the tears were in her eyes: for she was as fond of him as she could be of anyone. And then she was so pretty.

It was a few days after Asdis was gone that Hundi was late in his chamber, though their porridge stood ready for breakfast: and when he came, "What, man," cried Thorstein, "it's no Thing to-day: and thou with thy best clothes donned."

"Well, lad," answered Hundi, "it's a fine morning, and I just thought mayhappen we might be riding over to Asmundarlea, and I might as well be ready first as last."

Thorstein blushed. "I don't care if I do," said he.

"Well said," cried Halldora clapping her hands. "Here, sup thy pottage, Thorstein, good lad; and then don thy red silk kirtle that ye bought in Londonburg. No lass could say nay to thee in that."

So by noon they were at Greenodd door to ask Orm to go with them. For it was the custom when a man went a-wooing to take all his folk with him; not only to show that everything was fair and above-board, and to have witnesses of the word given on both sides, but also to show what good friends and kinsfolk he had to back him. For in times when wealth was held only by the strong hand, the best of havings was a good following of friends and friendly neighbours who would see one righted if need was.

But Orm said he was throng and could not come: and when they pressed him, he would not; and Unna said there was no need, for she warranted the job was no hard one to manage. So Hundi and Thorstein, with all their ship-crew, and all the farm servants that could be spared, rode over the fell, and knocked at Asmund's door.

They sat in the hall, and Asdis served them meat and drink, and Asmund sat in his high seat and talked of this and that, as though nobody knew on what errand they might be bound. It was an open winter: they settled that. And king Athelstan was dead : they talked that over. And folk seemed to take the new king, Eadmund they called him, a deal quieter than was expected. " Aye," said Asmund, " now is the time for decent quiet folk to be setting up house and settling down."

" Well, master," says Hundi, " it is a job of tha make brings us hither. My brother Thorstein here has made up his mind seemingly to take land and build house, the same as I have done : and he has the money, and the means, and all he wants is the mistress. And we were just thinking that if thy daughter could be spared, and if she would take to it kindly, she might happen do worse than settle down with my brother : and I am sure there's nought but he would do for her to make her happy ; and as to money matters, ye can suit yourselves."

Then master Asmund put on his sober face, and hemmed, and said, " Well, neighbour, it's a fair offer : but it's not for me to say aye or nay until we have spoken with the lass."

By this time the servants had fetched in Asdis, who had slipped out, as was proper, when things began to look like business. And there she was, blushing and rosy, standing by her father's seat, and plucking at her apron.

" Well, lass, and what are we to say ? Wilt thou take the young man Thorstein Sweinson ? For that's the job they have come about."

" Nay, father, it's not for me to say."

" Come, come, lass : that means aye ? "

" As you please, father : and as it pleases Master

Thorstein Sweinson. I am sure it is a great honour for the likes of me."

Then Asmund sent out to the neighbours, bidding them to a handfasting or betrothal feast, which should be held next day : and until then Hundi and Thorstein and their company were well entertained at Asmundarlea. In this while they talked over the dowry that Asdis should have from her father, and the settlement she should have from her husband, and when the wedding should be, and so forth.

When the neighbours were come, they bade them listen to the business on hand, and told them what had been done on both sides. Then Thorstein went over to where Asmund sat, and Asmund put his daughter's hand into the hand of Thorstein, who said aloud " We call upon all to witness that thou, Asdis Asmund's daughter dost lawfully pledge thyself to me Thorstein Sweinson, with dowry due and holden hands, to finish and fulfil our whole agreement both trusted and true. This handfasting is fairly done."

And so the wooing of Asdis was accomplished.

## CHAPTER XXXV

### HOW THORSTEIN TOOK
### LAND

HUNDI sat on his own howe, and Thorstein with him. They were looking out for neighbours who were to come to the new household where Hundi and Halldora were master and mistress.

" Dost thou mind when we were barns, brother, how we sat here and parted hence ? Seven winters have gone since we planned to keep house away yonder ; " and he pointed upbank, where the Crake came down between the crags on the right and the Blawith, the black wood as they called it, of dark firs mantling the long slopes of the lower banks, on the left. And far beyond were the great fells that surrounded the head of Thorstein's water, this Coniston lake that he, first of Northmen, had found.

The neighbours for whom they waited were coming to be witnesses to Thorstein's landtaking. It was the custom for settlers of uninhabited land to go round a tract of country, as much as they could encompass in a day, carrying fire, and lighting from point to point beacons which might be seen one from another. And when this was done with proper witnesses like any other deed of law, the land became the possession of that landtaker and his heirs for ever. Now up the Crake valley, above Lowick where Hundi had settled, there were no inhabitants at this time : whatever fell-folk used to hunt in the woods and fish in the waters dwelt upon the moors on either hand. It was Thorstein's mind to take all that upper valley between Lowick and the water-foot ; and he had bidden his neighbours to come and bear witness, so that there might be no dispute thenceforward. and that he and Asdis and his heirs might dwell there undisturbed in lawful freehold.

It was early in the morning of a bright frosty day, when the days were already a good bit longer than at Yule, that Thorstein and Hundi and his neighbours were already out, and at the bounds of Hundi's land before the sun was up. There was a company of half a score or so, dressed in their woodland dress of rough homespun, with axes in their hands ; and Thorstein himself carrying an iron pot with burning peat in it. They stood by the brink of the stream a little above Lowick force, and stamped their feet on the crispy sedges of the marsh-ground, until the sun should be up ; munching the remains of the hasty breakfast they had left, in order to be in good time and to make the most of the winter day. When the edge of the fell to the eastward blazed, and the sun began to get above the silver fringe of trees, a shapeless point of fire, " Away with us, friends," cried Thorstein ; and they made a move for the fell where the sun was standing, and started upbank through the trees that

clothed it, and over the scree that lay between.
Here and there they had to hew their way through
the underwood, and where that was not needed,
they marked the trees with great notches, in order
to leave no doubt of the boundary they had beaten.

As they passed along through the forest, where
every leaf was laced with rime, and the frozen twigs
crackled underfoot, beast and bird fled before the
noise of their axes and the loud talk and laughter of
the merry company. "A grand hunting-spot for
Thorstein the hunter," says one. "Oh, man,"
says another, "there went somewhat I'd be fain to
follow." "Never heed it, friend," said Thorstein;
"business is business. Wait till my house is built,
and then I'll show thee a day's hunting, and the
tricks I learned with the fell-folk."

When they came out on the ridge, they could
overlook the whole valley, and down into the next
where Colton stands and southward away to
Legbarrow. Here some of them began to cut
elding and logs to build a balefire, and others rolled
up a huge boulder to be planted on end for a meer-
stone or land-mark. And when the fire blazed up,
they lost no time, but set out again along the ridge,
up and down, until at last they came to a high
place overlooking the foot of Thorstein's water.
To most of them the sight was wholly strange, well
known as it was to him. The mere was just as he
had seen it seven years before; just as quiet and as
wild; only now it lay dark blue between its white
promontories; the shores were disguised with
shelves of ice that stood far out into the ripple, and

countless birds flew screaming about over the open spaces, or dived and settled in flocks.

On this high point, for the morning was beginning to wear, they built another balefire, and set up another meer-stone; and then picked their way down to the water-foot, where they came about midday, travelling but slowly, for the way was hard to find, and rough. At the crossing of Crake, where mere ends and beck begins, they ate hastily the bannocks they had brought with them; and Thorstein wading into the shallows with his fire-pot in one hand and a brand lighted at it in the other, cast the brand into the water; and as it floated hissing, cried out, " I take you to witness that this water and all its shores, oyce and ere, dub and deep, are hereby in my holding."

Then they started again along the western bank, and so up into the moor, where they built another beacon and set another meer-stone. But here Thorstein bade them turn, for he said that thence-beyond he reckoned he would be within the bounds of old friends, namely the fell-folk of Heathwaite. And he would have no disputes with them. " For we Northmen," said he, " have land enough in the wooded bottoms, and can well afford to leave the moor-tops to the wild folk who dwell there."

So they came round in a great half-moon under the brow of the moor, leaving the heather and enclosing the woods : and at last by sunsetting they were back again where they started from. Thorstein took them to witness that he had lawfully carried fire around untenanted land, and the land was thenceforth his and his only. And so after due feasting at Hundi's, the neighbours went their ways; and Thorstein, with such as were in his service, began the building of his house.

On the slope of the great black fir-wood, that rose to a howe behind and fell to the Crake in front, beside a little beck, they cleared a thwaite, and made the timber of it into a house. It was no long job to skilled wood-wrights, and with plenty of hands; for Thorstein's wealth got him all he wanted, what with buying thralls, and hiring free men who lay by the fire for the most part in winter. The house was like the Greenodd house; a great hall with little nooks built along each side of it for bed-chambers; high roofed and thatched with broom; and the walls, where the roughly squared logs left chinks open to the wind, daubed with clay and roughcast. A few outbuildings, byres and sheds, were put up to begin with; and round about the whole a dyke was raised and set with stakes, to keep out wild beasts and to make some stand against enemies, if such should ever appear. But who would expect foes in so lone and peaceful a spot?

By cuckoo-tide, or Gowk-month as the Northmen called it, the house was standing, and wanted but little; and that chiefly what a body might do after the flitting. And on the right flitting-days, that is to say about Whitsuntide as we should call it, they began to move goods into the house, carrying in first of all the salt and meal, and starting a fire upon the hearth. Since beds and benches were built there as fixtures, there was little to carry in the way of movable furniture, and what there was came in kists on horseback. And when all was flitted, there was nought to hinder the wedding.

# CHAPTER XXXVI

## THE WEDDING OF THORSTEIN

ON the day appointed, Thorstein and his men, dressed in their best, to make all the show they could, and carrying food and drink, rode out a good way from the house to meet the bride, who came riding with her father and kinsfolk and bridesmaids by the old track to Lowick. At the border of Thorstein's land they met, and alighting from their horses ate and drank to the good luck of the place they were come to. Then they made their procession, two and two on horseback, through the Blawith. The bride and bridegroom rode together at the head of the procession, and right glad was Thorstein to think that at last he would have house and wife of his own.

"Well, sweetheart," said he, "and now it's home."

"Is it always like this?" said she. "One would say it does nought but rain in your fells."

"No such thing," said he; "whiles it snows. But never mind; there's a warm hearth hard by. Thy riding cape will soon dry on the rannalbalk."

"Like a man! to put my cape in the soot indeed.

And what for a road call you this ?  Who will ever come to visit one, away here ? "

" Oh, there's Halldora ; she's a good neighbour, and no pleasanter visitor could we have."

" I'm thinking there's been a deal of Halldora lately."

" Well," said he, " come, Asdis, it'll be all right when we get there.   See, yonder's the little house."

If the day was dull and cheerless, bright lights were shining through the windows that evening, and a plentiful feast was made in Blawith hall.   In the chief high-seat was set Master Asmund, and beside him the neighbours who had been bidden to the wedding.   Over against him the bridegroom sat in his high-seat, with his men on either hand : and on the bride-bench, set across the hall at the upper end, was the bride, all dressed in white linen, with a high white cap and a white veil hanging down her back, with a silver brooch on her brow, a gold necklace at her throat, and house-wife's keys clattering at her girdle.   Beside her sat the brides-maids and her friends, with Unna and Halldora on the right hand and the left.

After they were set and the feast was well begun, Thorstein rose and went across the hall to his bride, and gave her for a bench-gift a cloak lined with rare furs and richly embroidered.   Then they drank to him and his bride, wishing them luck and long life, and with all the lights lit saw them to their lock-bed chamber ; at the door of which her father Asmund gave her with a fitting word into her husband's keeping.

The next morning, as the custom was, the marriage settlements were finished. Thorstein made over to Asmund the gifts that had been agreed upon, and Asmund put them in the keeping of the bride, to be her own property. And folk said that Thorstein had done well by Asmund's daughter, and that no lass of those parts could wish for a better husband. Then they went on to keep the wedding for three days with feasting and games and every pleasure that could be got for them. But still it rained, and they took to playing indoors, mating men, and wrestling in the hall, and skin-pulling across the fire spot, and draught-playing, and story-telling, and song-singing, and all that a body might do to pass the time.

But before the three days of the feast were well over, came a loud rapping at the door, and there stood a man holding the arrow to bid them to the midsummer meeting, which was to be in some three weeks. They made him welcome to the wedding, for they were fain of somewhat new.

" Nay," said he, " I reckon you will think twice of your welcome when you hear me out."

" Why so ? " cried they all.

" For the reason that our bonny bridegroom here will have to choose between a far journey and a fair bride, unless he stands out of the play, and I doubt he will never do that. At last, neighbours, there is a chance of some ado, and that speedily, if you take the counsel of them that sent me. You must know that when King Athelstan died, no hand was raised against him that followed, Eadmund etheling that was, king that is: and all things seemed to be even as they had been. But why or how I know not, Eadmund could never abide Northmen, and in especial he hates king Eric, him they call Bloodaxe, whom Athelstan had set over York. So when the word came to York that Eric was like to be turned out of his place, he never waited for Eadmund, but went forth and sailed away out of the Humber: and men say that he has gone north to Orkney where Arnkell and Erlend Einarsons are his friends."

"Like to like," says Thorstein; "and a good riddance too."

"That's as it turns out. For it's ill mending bad with worse. The York folk seemingly think any change lightsome, if its nobut out of bed into beck, as the old body said. What have they done but sent to Dublin bidding Olaf Guthferthson—"

"Plague on it," says Thorstein: "if it had been old Thorfin, or young Hakon, but a Dane!"

"Hear me, I say. Olaf the Dane, being of the old stock of Ivarsons, is bidden to take the power: and that speedily, before the young king can step in. And as Eadmund is but a lad of eighteen winters and no more, it is thought the Danes will have a chance of setting up once again in England. Now the Cumberland Welsh mislike it, and our friends thereaway mislike it; but they look to see the whole job done in the twinkling of an eye. And for you, if you have anything to say about it, now is your time."

So they asked what was to be done: and he said

that it was likely Olaf would come in with no very great following, by the old road from Ellenburg through Cumberland; and Domhnall was to be there to meet him, but whether as friend or foe was yet to be seen. And if the Northmen wished to have a hand in the matter, they should be at their Thing-stead at once, to take counsel with themselves and their neighbours, and to be ready for Olaf by the time he came into the defensible road among the fells.

"What, Thorstein," said Asdis, "you are never going on this fool's errand, and me nought but half wed?"

"Why, lass, it is but a three days' run, and I'll be back again in a hop, skip and jump."

Something seemed to come before him as he spoke: as when in a dream one says, "All this I have dreamt before." Then he remembered; and turned away.

## CHAPTER XXXVII

## THORSTEIN SEES GHOSTS

"AND so, friends," said King Domhnall, ending his speech, " we betake ourselves to Penrith, and if the men of Athacliath come in peace, it shall be peace : but if in war, war let it be."

Then all the Northmen took their weapons and shouted aye to what he had said : and the meeting broke up, and men moved away in groups towards the deep dale that led eastward. Some sought their horses, and some were for lading their gear : and everything was in hurry and turmoil.

"Hundi," said Thorstein, leaning on his brother's shoulder, " Seest thou yon fell ? Up yonder are the houses where the beauty lives : and behind it is the giant's castle, where I was with— with her that's gone. Little did I think when we fled away over fells and dells and mountain moors, how it would end with all of us."

"Leave thy maundering man, and come to see what uproar is yonder," said Hundi ; for among the men left behind by the main guard there were shrieks and shouts, that seemed to mean no good. It was but a step, and they found among the rough followers of Domhnall, struggling and crying, who but Aluinn ? whom they rescued, not without hard knocks. But still she went on like one wild, and it was long before they could get reasonable speech out of her. As they led her away, sore against her will it seemed, in spite of the mis-handling she had got, they heard her story bit by bit.

What came out was this :—that she had gone like any other to the camp where the Welsh king lay, and coming to his tent door was for marching in. Who but she had the right, indeed ? But within was another woman, with two sturdy lads at her knees, and a fair woman too. " Who is this ? " says the woman. " Who is this ? " says Aluinn, and shows the collar of gold that certain lover once gave her. With that the wife bids her begone for a slut ; and then Aluinn gives her words, and gets to blows : when in comes Domhnall with little love in his looks, and to make short work of it, turns her out to his rascals.

" The nithing ! " cries Hundi. Thorstein said little, but set his teeth and growled, remembering what was heard and said at Alclyde.

But when the fell-folk heard the tale, Aluinn's own neighbours whose pet and pride she was, you may guess if they vowed vows and threatened threats. As they shook their weapons Hundi plucked his brother by the sleeve. " We do no good here," said he, " and may come to harm. Hie thy ways along with me, or we are shamed men at the tryst." So they got off without leavetaking, and footed it down the dale : for their nags were gone in the tumult, and not a soul in sight.

Along the dale they passed, bemired as it was with

the trampling of man and horse in that foul weather, and at every wath the beck was a torrent. But since the track lay fairly high on the fell-side it lay dry, if aught was dry, and was not lost in swamp like the flats in mid dale. In the space of an hour or two they spied a great flickering of weapons and hings waving, and guessed that the kings had already met, and spoken each other fair, and were now settling down for the night : for they could spy tents going up and smoke starting. And so in a while they were among their friends, supping and singing round a fire in the open, until men dropped off one by one to sleep where they sat.

But Thorstein slept little for thinking of Aluinn and her wrongs. She was as it were a ghost of his old life come back from the dead, and little ease it gave to think of those times, and then again of these. For, thinking of Aluinn, he could not but think of Raineach who was dead : and how he had loved her, and how fain he would be if he could but get the sight of her face once more. " Ah my dear," he cried, half aloud, and opened his arms and turned over on his side, for his heart was sore within him. But only the heap of snoring soldiers lay around, under the lowering cloud. And yet, what was that face that flitted over the heap, gleaming in the red glow ?

His blood ran cold to the finger-tips, and he clenched his hands. He had wished, and his wish had come to pass. It was her ghost, he thought : for ghosts come when they are called. The hair tingled on his head, he was so terrified. Then he shut his eyes tight, and drew up his knees, and doubled his arms over his face, and lay there for a while, still as a hedgehog when it is scared, and curls itself up.

At last the terror began to die away. He said to himself that it was but his own thoughts his eyes had seen; and he could not help looking again. There was a gap in the clouds, and a star. The fire was not so bright, Nothing did he see beyond the men who lay around, though he fixed his eyes on the spot where the vision had been, as if he dared it to come again. But it came not. By and by there was a stir behind him, as of the wind rising in the trees. He turned sharply round, and there!

But it was gone again: and once more he lay quaking, with cold in all his limbs, and in his heart an agony which he could not understand, like a child when it is beaten for something it has not done, and cannot tell the truth: blank misery as when one is utterly spent with sickness. He lay staring at the black cloud overhead, and it was an ugly thing coiling over him. He shut his eyes and dreamed over the days of long ago: of the wild, proud slip of a girl that hunted and fished with him at Greenodd: of the poor little ugly, blubbered face that leaned over his, when he was a child captive in the giant's hut on the fells; the tears that made dirty water-courses among the freckles—how he remembered them, and every eager feature he had loathed at first and loved ever after. He brought to mind how he had opened his eyes after his sickness, wearily and lazily; and then!

## CHAPTER XXXVIII

## RAINEACH'S STORY

"Hush," she said, "don't crush me, or we shall stumble over yon snoring swine. Hither, lad: away with me. Into the wood. It was always our hiding-place—dost thou mind, Thorstein? Why, what a man thou hast grown! But I knew I should tell thee among them all, wolf-dark as it was. Kiss me, Thorstein. Am I woman enough for thee now? Am I bonny? Folk say so; but I'd have none but thee, heart of mine. Thorstein, Thorstein: my boy, my little hurt beaten boy. Ah, but I will comfort thee. Laugh lad, never greet: kiss me. Oh Thorstein, kill me not: I am only a woman, and thou art a great strong man.

"The queen told me about thee. They say she wept for a day and a night when thou wast gone, until Olaf the carle gave her a slap and bade her be merry. If thou could'st but have stayed until I got there; it was but a few days. Silly lads to run away from friends! And yet thou would'st have loved the bonny queen, and poor Raineach was but her bowermay: but fain, ah fain to serve thee and her, anywhere, any way. But it was so long a-coming, lad!

"Oh me, I am losing my wits. Only have

patience, and I will tell thee all as it happened. There, loose me awhile, and let me think.

" Orm, it was. Orm said I must tell nobody, but I'll tell thee, sweetheart. Orm said thou wast oversea, and bade me come. So I went. I took all our bravest things to make a show at the wedding. He set me on shipboard, and bade the skipper have a care of me, and signed farewell off the shore. And then the waves beat and the wind blew, and eh, my head worked, and the eyes came out of their pits. They thrust me down among the bulk, and among poor wretches that howled and groaned in the bilgewater, and I could see nothing for sickness. The ship whirled, and flew, and fell into the depths of the sea. Oh, lad, I was sorry for thee in those terrible ships ; and I prayed and prayed to have thee safe on dry land. And there were poor Welsh lasses and a two or three Saxon ones, worse off than I, with hands tied : and I loosed them, I did. And then came the skipper and clouted me over the head, and tied us all again, and I was mad with him, and begged and shouted ; but he laughed, like Orm when he kicks his thralls and bade me be at peace, or he would throw me to the fishes. Eh, it did hurt to have one's hands tied. Did'st thou ever have thy hands tied, Thorstein ? and kick and scream at people ? The other poor wretches laughed at me, and said things, but I could make nothing of their talk. And so I was still, for anger and weariness, all that night.

" Well, when it was day, I was no more sick, the water was lound, and the men were rowing us to

shore. Then they gave us food, and the skipper
said I was to look bonny, or I would fetch nothing
on Dublin strand, and shame it were if all his
labour and all the money he had spent and the care
he had taken of me should be thrown away. He
said we should be very thankful to be there at all,
for in the storm of that night other ships had gone
to the bottom of the sea. I could not hit him, for
my hands were tied, so I spat out the food they put
in my mouth, and I looked as ugly as I could ; and
he beat me. Oh man, I was angry.

" Then they shoved us over the side of the ship
and set us down in a great crowd of people, but I
was too dazed to take notice. At last came a fine
lady ; that was the queen, understand. King's
folk have first weel of the wares in Dublin town.
I was the wares, Thorstein : think of that, lad. I
couldn't think : but I cried to her in my own
tongue, I am not a thrall, I am not a thrall : I am
Thorstein Sweinson's sister.

" ' What ? girl, ' " said she : and I said it again.

" Then there was a deal of talking with the
skipper, and my hands were untied, and they
tingled all over, and I could feel nothing with them.
But I made shift to creep after the queen : and she
led me to the king's house, and oh she was good to
me : and it was a bonny spot, if it had not been for
the men-folk plaguing. There's none of them like
thee, lad. I could tell thee things about yon Olaf—
but what's the good ? I am woman grown now,
and bonny ; and I can sew and bake and brew and
everything. Thy mother will be pleased with me

now, and Orm, won't he be surprised ? Are they all hearty, Thorstein ? And that young lass, does she still play her tricks on folk ? how did they call her—Asdis ? "

Thorstein's arms fell and his knees smote together.

" What's to do, lad ? "

" Three days since—I wedded her."

" Thorstein ! " she cried in a terrible voice, and thrust him away from her, and fled. He fell backward, like one that has got his death-stroke.

## CHAPTER XXXIX

## ORM PAYS

I⊤ was high day, and he lay there slowly coming to himself; and recalling that dreadful nightmare, as it seemed, bittersweet. At last he staggered to his legs, and drank at a beck that ran through the wood. Every one was gone from the spot where the camp had been : and whither ? He only knew that Orm would be with the Northmen faring homeward. He loosened his sword and thrust it back again, and stumbled forth along the road he had come but yesterday.

On their way home, at Legburthwaite the North-men had halted, to hold their Thing, to talk over the business that had passed, and finish the work they had on hand. On a little hillock the chiefs were assembled, within the hallowed ring that no man might profane.

Thorstein leaned on the hazel rods, that stood as bars from stake to stake to encompass the place. Some one was speaking in slow, steady tones, and men were listening, in the rain, with grave faces, intent upon the speech.

" Orm Sweinson, come forth. News for thee : ha ! ha ! " cried a voice, breaking the quiet of the assembly : and there was a haggard man with bloodshot eyes, beckoning strangely.

Forth stepped Orm : " What now ? youngster,"
said he.

" Raineach is come again, and that's for thee ! "
screamed Thorstein, lashing his sword through the
throat of his brother, where the coat of mail left it
unshielded.

" A wolf, a wolf in the temple ! " they shouted,
and rushed forth.   But he was gone headlong down
the bank and across the lake-foot and into the woods
on the other side, on the rugged slopes of the Benn.

## CHAPTER XL

## A DOOR-DOOM

UNDER Blawith roof-tree sat dame Asdis, fresh and
fair as a daisy; and when she had broken her fast
she looked to her outdoor servants and set them
their tasks; and when she had put them all in
order, she came in, at the time folk take their
drinkings; and she drank a horn of ale, and ate
sweet cakes, one after another, and then she washed
her hands at the trough by the porch and got he
a clean apron and sat down in her high-seat, and
took to her sewing; and if the day was hot, and
she dropped off to sleep while one might count
two score, it was no shame to her, now she was
wedded woman and ever a house-wife of the most
notable. And then she wished Halldora would
come to pay her a visit. For it was nought but
dull in these backwoods, and news was worth
whittlegate. So she went to the door to see if the
weather was holding up, and sure enough it had
brightened, as it does sometimes at mid-day after
stormy weather, and the lift was lighter than
heretofore. The rain had stopped, and the beck
was roaring white.

" Who comes tramping over the lea land ? Hey
lads, a stranger. Run for your weapons. What,
not Thorstein, surely ? and all so draggled and

dabbled? Wenches, here's the master, and a pretty pickle he is in. A bath is the next thing; but fetch me the ale-tub and the biggest horn first."

For you see she knew the ways of menfolk to a tittle, to treat them high and low as they should be treated.

"Well, Thorstein," says she, as he came up to the door, "here's a conny mess. Sit in the porch, man, and the ale will be here gey soon. Thou art not fit to touch before a bath and a shift of clothes; and I can't have that filthment of a kirtle on thy new high-seat bolster, thou know'st. Eh, these men, they are nought but great barns. Now, Thorstein, what hast thou been doing?"

He leaned back and drank off the ale, and looked at her strangely.

"I have killed Orm," said he.

"None of thy jokes, lad. Say a better word. How is this? That the bonny bridegroom could wait no longer; eh, lad? and made more haste worse speed homeward?"

"But it's truth," said he.

"What's truth? Gods forbid. And when, and where?"

"At the Thing," said he.

"Killed Orm at the Thing?" she cried. "Is he daft? It's outlawing!"

"Then I am outlawed," said he, drinking again.

"Thorstein, how darest thou? And me but new wed. Man, this caps aught. Unsay it, lad, and never torment me."

"There is nought to unsay; it was his due; and I'd kill him again if he came to life."

"Came to life? Folk never come to life," said she, scornfully.

"They do, though."

Asdis was pale as grass, staring like a stone woman for a while. Then she was red as blood, and looked this way and that, and at last muttered something about the ale being over strong on an empty belly. Thorstein looked at her in wonder. Then she burst out: "Who has come, then? Nay, I care not for thy hints nor thy threats, thou false thing that never was true to me. Away with thee! Who will believe a word from a wolf's head? Who dare say I had a hand in it? What have I done, tell me that? What did Orm say, the liar?"

"Orm said nothing. Maybe Asdis has said a word too much," answered Thorstein, rising from his seat and going into the house.

"Thorstein, my dear, Thorstein!" said she, "I meant nought; I said nought."

But he slammed the door of his lockbed in her face, and shot the heavy bars, and would not come out for all she cried.

It was late in the afternoon that horses clattered into the garth, and there were Asmund and Hundi and a dozen of neighbours, who three days ago had been the wedding guests, and had ridden away from Blawith to the Althing. Asdis came out to meet them, with the smile she always had ready, and ale was standing in the porch. But they would not drink, and she was outfaced and browbeaten by their stern looks.

"My poor child, it's ill news we bring," said Asmund. "Is Thorstein Sweinson within?"

"And what's to do with Thorstein Sweinson, father?"

"I fear me he will be man of thine no more, if peace-breaking gets its due. We are here—thou knowest, child, it is sore against our wills—to summon him for breaking the peace of the Thing by slaying his brother Orm; and we would know, in all kindness to himself, for what cause he did the deed."

"What, father? This caps aught! It cannot be."

"Nay; as to the deed we were all in a way to witness; for it was done hard by the Thing-bounds. But what was said none heard."

She clasped her hands until her fingers cracked, and caught her breath; then she broke out, "The villain to kill his brother. Oh, me, that I am wedded to such a man: a wolf's head that is to be. Oh, father, take me away and get me free of him."

"What, is he here?"

She pointed to the door of the lockbed; but no man stirred, for they might not enter with the strong hand until doom had been given. So they cried out to him, but got no answer.

Then stood forth Asmund, for he was chief man amongst them, after Orm, and after Hundi who might happen inherit, but now hung back. Said Asmund:

"Neighbours, a foul thing has been done, no less than the breaking of the Thing-peace. Ye know our old use and wont : for how could we have law or counsel else, unless the Thing were hallowed from all violence and the peace-breaker put out of the peace of all true men. And this is doubly foul, for he that was slain was our chief ; and trebly, for it was his brother slew him unoffending, so far as we know, and unprepared as you all saw. Now stand we here over against the door of his house, and give doom."

So they drew a few paces back to give room for the accused to stand with his friends at his door, if he would appear ; and for a loaded wain, so the old custom was, to pass between the two parties. And they named Asmund their lawman, and he named six to give judgment, who took oaths that they would judge right. Then he stated the case, and shouted aloud to Thorstein to come forth, and speak up for himself.

But when no answer was given, Hundi stood up and said, "Friends, you are too hasty. It is never our way to doom a man unheard ; and if any has the right to speak it is I, who stand here between brother and brother. Of him that is dead, I would speak no ill ; but ye know him. Of him that lives I have no ill to speak. Ye know him not as I do ; and here I say that against all seeming I hold him sackless and sinless."

With that there was a shouting against Hundi, that he was always in a tale with Thorstein, and both were runagates and had turned Christians abroad, and there was no trusting them. Shame it was to Hundi that he would not take up the vengeance for his brother, and do right by the laws. Some cried out that he should be charged with abetting the manslaughter.

"Nay," said Asmund, "peace, friends. Hear me. This let us do. Put Hundi in keeping, and harm him not; but let the jury give doom."

So they encompassed Hundi and bore him down with their shields, and took his weapons, and led him out and bound him; while the six men gave their doom that Thorstein Sweinson had broken the Thing-peace, and slain his brother their chief, and for that he was put out of law.

Then Asmund gave out their finding, and said moreover that he put the wonted price of a hundred of silver on the wolf's head, dead or alive. And then, for the sun was nigh its setting, they pressed into the house, no man withstanding them, and made for the door where he lay, to kill him, as the law was, while it was still day. They brought a great beam of wood and battered it against the panels, swinging it between them, while others ran round to keep the back of the house.

All this while Thorstein lay quiet, and gave no sign, like a fox in its bield while folk twine the screws to draw him out; and still they battered, for the door was new built, and strong. And still Hundi lay in bonds without, struggle and shout as he might.

"And thou, Asdis," he cried, "shame on thee to leave thy husband to his slayers—shame and evil on thee! Ill befall the finger that betrayed him, and the tongue that spoke never a word while they doomed him; and mischance on the gear that thou art shifting from his house. I see thee, woman, and thy tricks; thou robbing and thy kin murdering. Shame and scathe on the scrow of ye!"

For Asdis had bidden her servants carry out all her goods, seeing very clearly what was forward, because she was a wise woman. By this time she had loaded horse and man with bales and arks, and away down the road homeward, saying nothing to Hundi's curses; which was the easier, for by now the door was battered in amid great tumult, and Thorstein was standing there, at blows with his pursuers. One lay on the ground at his feet among the wreckage; and a couple more sat in the hall, out of the fray, nursing ugly wounds.

"Hold, boys," shouted Asmund, "we are but spending good stuff." They drew back, seemingly as eager to keep Thorstein in now as they were to get him out before. They began to drag tables and benches to block the passage and pin him down, and then they got fire from the hearth and all the elding they could compass, and cast it among the splinters of the burst panelling and the lockbed-door. And soon the bed was ablaze, with such a smoke that they were glad to get out of the house; and there they stood in the twilight, watching the flames catch the roof, and grimly waiting for Thorstein to rush out and get his death wound, or to hear his last cry in the fire.

Q

The wind had shifted to the north-west, now that the weather was holding up; and it drove the smoke of the new green wood in a great whirl by the door of the house, which was set, as always, to catch the morning sun. The men were forced to give it a wide berth; but sure they were that he could not escape, and so fierce against him that not one of them had a thought but burn and kill. They got victuals from the out-bowers, remnants of the wedding feast, and emptied the ale-tub from the porch, and rubbed their hands while the long tongues of flame wavered into the air against the stars, and the forest behind showed every branch and leaf in the glow; the crackling and spitting dinned in their ears, and the smoke was red in coils against the black sky.

There they watched until the fire died down; and said Asmund, " Lads, we have done a good deed, for to ash he will be burnt in yon cinder heap. As for the price, as we have all shared the work, let us share the pay. Come home with me and see if I keep my word. And thou, Hundi Snail, never show thy face again, unless to thank thy best friends for ridding thee of thy worst foe. I take all to witness that justice has been done, and nought but justice."

## CHAPTER XLI

### WOLF'S HEAD

FOREDONE with his anger, Hundi crept home to Lowick by the dawn of the day, and told the gruesome tale to Halldora. She, good soul, wept bitterly for Thorstein, and most of all for the part she had taken in mating him with that false and heartless minx. When she had her fill of weeping, she looked up and ran forth of the house as she was, like one bewitched.

The day was far spent when she came back, queer to look at.

"Is there any quarrel between thee, Hundi Sweinson, and thy brother?"

"Nay," said he. "Would not I have saved him, but I was bound?"

"And if he had fled?" says she, between laughing and crying.

Aye, there he was, at the door, bemired and bloody with wounds, and the hair of his head singed off him, and his eyes nigh bleared away with the fire through which he had fled. But she had found him in the woods, and comforted him, and wormed a true tale out of him, and led him home. There he was and there he stayed in safe hiding, for Lowick was an outlying spot, with no passing; so they nursed him for weeks until he was whole again.

But if his body was whole, his heart was hardened, and never a word would he speak of good or ill, after that first talk in the wood with kind Halldora.

Now Halldora's one hope was to see this wrong righted; all the rather because she could not help blaming herself for the hasty wedding. But it was not easy. For there sat Thorstein like a log, and if he showed his face it would be death to him and shame to them. Hundi was a good boy and no fool, but he was not to be sent on ticklish errands, she knew that. And now she was tied, for there was a lusty urchin, Thorstein Hundason by name, in her arms, with a face as round as the harvest moon that rose up night after night over Colton fell.

So one fine day came to Greenodd door the Lowick folk, with a led horse, bidding Unna to visit her first grandchild, which she could not refuse. And when Halldora had got her as pleased with all as she could be, out came the story of Thorstein; not easily, for at first Unna was woe and wrath at her son's death, and would hear nothing to excuse the slayer. But who can say nay to a mother with her first babe newborn? and Thorstein was ever the best loved and longest lost of the three. Unna's eyes were opened, and when she came upon her boy, so beaten down and disheartened that he scarce knew her, she could do nothing but weep over him. And going home she sent for her brother Raud and set the case before him, and made him a promise of the chieftainship which had now fallen into her hands to bestow as she liked. And so he was brought into the business.

And then Halldora sent for her father, Master Grimkel Mani, and won him over likewise. And they plotted that when the autumn Thing was held, Raud should be made chief and be there with a great following. Then Mani should come with all he could bring, and a round sum of money, which Unna would find, to get Thorstein's outlawry taken off; and Hundi should confirm the true tale, and back up the suit.

But in the meanwhile, what with all this going and coming, and the tattling of thralls, it leaked out that Thorstein was not dead after all; and that the men who had burnt Blawith were but fools for their pains. Asmund sent a furious message to Hundi to warn him of the danger of harbouring an outlaw; and bade him look for visitors some night when he did not want them. Hundi was greatly put about, but Halldora laughed, and said that she knew Asdis would never forgive Thorstein for finding her out. Grimkel Mani sent some of his biggest men to bide at Lowick, in case they might be wanted; and they slept with one eye open.

Well, the day came for the Thing, and folk were there from far and wide in their feast array, and everyone that could be spared of Thorstein's kin together with their people. Before the meeting,

Unna feasted the elders and householders at Greenodd, and sat among them in her widow's weeds ; and after the tables were cleared she bade them to witness that through her son's death the chieftainship had fallen to her ; that, alas, one of her sons was outlawed, and the other was ill looked upon by neighbours, so that she could name neither of them to the office ; whereupon she would give the place to her brother Raud, who lived hard by, and was an able man, and would see that the Thing was kept up with due offerings to the gods, and entertainment to all comers, and so forth.

Now this was not just what the other party would have liked, but they could not gainsay it, and away they moved to the Thing-field. Then Raud, as the custom was, killed a ram, and reddened his hands in the blood of it, taking at the same time the oath of office ; and so after due hallowing of the spot, sat him down on the topmost seat.

Then stood Asmund on the one side and Mani on the other, each claiming to be heard. The new chief ruled that Asmund should have the first word, for he thought it wise to let them talk it well out. So Asmund set forth that his daughter Asdis being wedded to a man who had been outlawed, claimed to be released from him, and to take all that belonged to her, namely the third of land and goods.

For you must know that in those heathen days, among the Northmen, the wife was master. She had her own goods and land to herself, and could sell them for her own use; even against the husband's will she could make away with the full half. And yet he had to manage it all, and to manage it well; and to defend it and her in every way. They were grand times for the women-folk. A wife could turn off her husband like a hired servant, for almost anything that displeased her. And there was nothing a man could do in law that the woman could not do as well, or better. Now Asdis might have just turned off her husband, with a word, when she left him; but she would not then have had a claim on his land. So being a wise woman she held her tongue, and now brought this suit against him.

There were witnesses to the outlawing at the door-doom, and there was little defence made; for nobody of Thorstein's friends wished to bind him to the woman; and as for land, there was plenty more to be taken, if she made a point of holding to a bit of uncleared timber.

This business being done, the other put in his plea. He was a hearty carle, was Grimkel Mani— Master Moon we might call him by interpretation. With his great grey beard, and his tall figure some-what barrowbacked, he was well listened to at meetings, and much respected by high and low, but no great hand at cunning and trickery. When he began to speak of Thorstein there was a dis-turbance. At last Raud got peace, and the suit went forward. Mani told how Thorstein had not been heard in his defence—how could he, standing alone and all his foes about him? And then he went on to tell the other side of the story, how Raineach had saved Thorstein as a lad, and had been received by his people as a sister; how Orm had been a rough kinsman to all his house, and a hard master to his folk; and how he had tricked Raineach into thralldom, and made up a lying tale about it.

So far so good; though it was no new story for a stranger, man or wench, to be sold off as useless or troublesome rubbish. But then Mani went on to complain that the doom of outlawry had been unlawfully given; for the crime was done at the Althing, said he, and to the Althing the case should be taken. He said, moreover, that so great a penalty as full outlawry should not have been laid at a door-doom, which was meant for little cases, such as the distraint of goods from a refractory debtor, and such like. Then he said that the attack had been continued after sunset, and therefore if they had killed Thorstein it would have been murder. " And all this," said he, " comes of the folly of men I see sitting over yonder, who have let themselves be led from on bad to worse by a wicked woman."

Then there was a terrible to-do. Men ran for their weapons; and the only way of saving the Thing-stead from blood was for Raud to break up the meeting, and draw off his friends; begging them to be guided and to save their strength for another chance.

Thorstein at Blawith heard the news as one who heeds little. He thanked them for their kindness, and said he must be going, for he would not bring them into straits. And so Hundi set him on his way across the Leven, and Raud kept him for a night, and asked him whither bound. Thorstein said he had a mind to go far. It was in his heart to go in search of Raineach, even if he had to lait her at York and in the house of the king there; but after her anger he feared and doubted, though he said nothing.

"Kinsman," said Raud, "take my counsel. Things have gone against thee, but the tide will turn. Thou hast friends, and good ones, and when the truth gets ground and springs up, it will bear fruit, never fear. We were in error to open the case anywhere but at the Althing; but we shall try again and get thee cleared at last, in spite of that woman and her witch-face. It is only a fool that throws his oars overboard when his tiller snaps. Now go not far. Over yonder in Cartmel is out of our bounds. None of our Northmen will touch thee there; but when good news is to be sent, thou wilt not be hard to seek."

## CHAPTER XLII

## CARTMEL

CARTMEL was the land between the Kent and the
Leven, given long before to St. Cuthbert and still
owned by his successors in the bishopric. In
Thorstein's time there was a big village of Welsh
at Walton, where much later St. Michael's Church
and then the Priory were built, but the chapel of
St. Cuthbert's monks was at Kirkhead, between
Blenket and the sea, where the old way over the
sands came to the shore. There, not so long ago,
could be found forgotten graves and the traces
of that earliest church, and there came Thorstein,
seeking sanctuary.

A man in a long gown was pulling at a rope and
ringing the bell. It tinkled in the quiet air, above
the shouts of children on the green, to the brown
woods of the hills that lay around, and the distant
murmur of the incoming tide, and up into the
golden evening sky.

It was but a twelvemonth ago that Thorstein
had been christened and taught the faith; but
since then, what things had happened? Dare he
now enter the church, he who had kept no day
holy nor heard mass, nor even latterly said the
prayers he used to say night and morning? It had
come to this that his stony heart was shut to man

and God alike. When Hundi and Halldora knelt, for she had learned her husband's faith—when they knelt to their cross, he would walk out of the way dowly enough. If his brother's blood was on his hands, that was little in an age when few men's hands were white; but there came over him a vague and terrible fear that he could not name to himself—the conscience of backsliding, the haunting of Hakon; and the words of the apple-garth at Ladir rose up in his mind, " Whoso denieth me." He could not say what he had then said to Hakon, nor take the answer. " You have preached to me," said the poor young king; and here he was, a castaway.

The bell stayed ringing, and there was a voice within, the sound that he knew well, of evensong. He sat down by the church door, rudely pillared in wood with some rough notching on it to imitate the carving of the great churches he had seen; and listened while Amen followed Amen like the noise of a beck in a gill. The children left playing, and stood round him out of arm's reach, to stare.

By and by the droning within stopped. A hand was laid on his shoulder.

" Who art thou, son?" said an English voice. But there was no answer.

" Who art thou, son?" it said again in Welsh.

" A wanderer."

" Returned?" said the priest.

Thorstein knelt before him and burst into sobs. The children had crept up behind the priest, and two or three were holding by his gown.

"Children, run home; it is supper-time for all of you," said the priest, making the sign of blessing over their rough white heads. "And thou, son, give me thy heart. It shall be in safe keeping."

He led Thorstein into his dwelling and set food before him, and bade him rest. In due time the lad's heart was opened, and he told his tale, or somewhat of it, so much as let it be known that he was born a heathen and baptised a Christian, but had fallen back; and that all was wrong with him now.

"Aye," said the priest, "for thy sin's sake. I spare thee not, for it is written, Whom the Lord loveth he chasteneth. But I smite thee not, for it is written again, Him that cometh to me I will in no wise cast out."

"Father," said Thorstein, "I have learned enough to know that a man may be made clean with penance from many a crime. Is there a penance strong enough for such as me?"

"Son," said he, "for every sin the church has penance, and for every sinner she has room. To confess thy sin is the first thing; to weep for it is the next; and what more is there but to bring forth fruits worthy of repentance? For thy back-sliding I bid thee dwell henceforward with Christians, and forsake the heathen and their ways. Fast and pray as it is commanded. And for the man-slaying thou hast done, if thou have told the truth about it, God alone will be thy Judge. It is not for me to bind or loose."

Thorstein slept that night, and awoke with a

new heart. After matins were done the priest brought him to the Reeve, praying that something might be given to put him in a way of living among Christian folk, for he was a penitent and a brand plucked from the burning.

The Reeve, a burly Englishman, servant of the See, and to all purpose lord of Cartmel, looked the stranger up and down.

"Well, my penitent," said he, "this is church land, and churchman's word is law here," said he. "But by thy looks I should name thee a church-robber, and no lamb of our flock. However," said he, "since father John there stands for thee, knowing the risks, I'll see to it. What can'st thou do, man?"

Thorstein said, very humbly for him, that he would put his hand to anything to addle whittle-gate : that he knew something about beasts, and smithying, and such like.

"In a word," said the Reeve, "man of all trades and master of none, or thou would'st not be here. But come thy ways, and I'll prove thee."

Sure enough he set him one job and another ; and if Thorstein was willing at the muck-heap, he was clever at the smithy ; until the Reeve laughed again, and clapped him on the back, saying : "Good lad. I never knew yon thieving, murdering rascals could turn out such a fellow!"

So he guested him in his house that winter, and took on with him as never was. And to cap all, when the spring was come, "Young man," said he, "folk can't be always on hand," said he.

" That they can't," said Thorstein wondering.

" And when they are gone they would like to lie easy, by the church yonder, and see things done right by the land ? "

" That they would," said Thorstein.

" Well," said he, " I am but the servant of the blessed Minster, and of the abbot yonder; but I think they owe me somewhat, and what with father John's good word and all we might manage it. Now, look here. There's none of these fellows fit to hold a candle to me and you, and none knows the land as they that live on it. Reason is when I drop off the best man should follow me ; and the abbot, he would say aye to that, if we got the soft side of him. Now, Master Thurstan, I've a daughter. She is a fine girl, though I say it who shouldn't; and a right good one, and the apple of my eye. But what, lad, thou hast set eyes on her. What then ? "

Thorstein thanked him kindly, and said it was more than he deserved.

" Not a bit, lad. There, think it over, and I'll answer for the wench."

Thorstein went to father John, for he was very thick with him, and never missed his church, fast-day or feast-day.

" Father," said he, " I would go on pilgrimage to York. Maybe a sight of the blessed Minster would do me good."

" Well said, my son : go in peace."

## CHAPTER XLIII

## AT YORK

YORK city was a wonderful place as one came upon it by the old North Road. From afar its towers rose up above the green tillage of the plain, beyond the winding Ouse; and as the traveller drew nearer, he saw the great high mound that encompassed the garth of houses, set with its bristling stockade above, and parted from the fields by a water-ditch as broad as a broad river. In the midst of this great wall was the North gate, through which the road ran, and within were houses and houses, some high, some low, some mean like the cottages at Cartmel, some stone-built and grand with painting and carving, but all cheek by jowl, as one may say, along the narrow winding streets, thronged with people and wares set out to sell, and foul with the refuse and rubbish of a thickly inhabited town.

Above the house-roofs rose a great building, the famous Minster, with its towers standing high over gable and pinnacle, graceful and slender. Up there the bells clanged above the din and hurry of the town in those dark, deep streets, like deep roaring gills and whirling torrents below.

But it was not for the Minster that Thorstein was bound, as he elbowed through the crowd, and picked his steps over the unpaved lane that was more gutter than path. He hardly dared question the wayfarers, such a stoore and a stir there seemed to be. But he knew that somewhere in the heart of the houses he should find Olaf's palace, the new castle that had been built after Athelstan destroyed the old Danish stronghold—the great hall where King Eric had sat with his witch-wife, and skald Egil the swart had sung the lay that won him his head.

So he went forward along the streets, with a beating heart and pale lips, towards the midmost of the city where the great towers rose. When he came before the castle there was an open space, and the houses fell back like trees from a green glade in the forest. But instead of coneys skipping in the grass, here was a great crowd gathered and a tumult going on. Out of every window round the place was a head thrust, and folk fringed the house-roofs a-straddle on the thatch-rigging, and all shouting at once. Stones were flying, and the shopkeepers at the corner, where Thorstein came into the square, were scrambling their goods under cover and shutting their shutters. It seemed as if the townsfolk of the baser sort were trying to force the castle doors, and whoever came out of the narrow streets, like rats out of their holes, thrust themselves on their fellows in front and shoved and shouted; and ill luck it would have been to have tripped in the midst of that scrimmage. Over heads and fists many a stick was waving; and here and there an axe, and here and there a sword, flashing in the sun-gleam, that now and then broke on the square through the rain-showers. On they came by hundreds; aye, by thousands, swarming; for the old books say that in those days no less than thirty thousand souls were crammed within the narrow walls that girt the city of York; so you may well believe there was no lack of hands, whether for peace or for fighting.

"What's to do, friend?" says Thorstein to a neighbour, who by the look of him was no Saxon, but a Dane; and a right hearty, well-to-do looking merchant man he seemed, now that he had got his goods shifted, and shutters up, and stood there with one hand holding his door ajar, and with the other gripping his axe.

"What's to do?" repeated the Dane; "why, it's the old story. A stranger, eh? none of the Saxon folk anyhow." For Danes and Northmen talked the same tongue, and foregathered among strangers.

"Nay," said Thorstein, "no Saxon, though a traveller from over the fells."

"No offence," said the Dane; "but one can't be too careful, with Southron spies all about. Our kinsman, thou knowest, friend, have no bed of roses in this bonny burg."

"I know nought," said Thorstein. "What is forward?"

"What thou seest, and I hope they may break the castle. For if the great doors yonder hold, they will sack the shops for want of a job. Thou hast heard, maybe, rumour that King Olaf is dead. To-day it is assured. It was somewhere in the

R

North, Tyningaham I think they called the spot. Look out, man!"

There was a rush towards the door, and stones flew. The Dane plucked Thorstein into the house, slammed the door, and made it fast with stout bars. Then he cast an eye on the bolts of his window, and laughed as they stood in the shop, lit only through the cracks in the shutters.

"It is a pretty stiff bit of oak," he said. "We shall hold out awhile, unless they take to fire-raising, and that would risk their own kennels. Well, as I was saying, Olaf being gone, we must have a new king. Some of these Saxon rubbish would be glad to see the Southrons in here; and, anyhow, they mean to make hay while the sun shines."

"So they are trying to plunder the king's house?" said Thorstein.

"That's it; but never heed them. I have seen three or four such ados in the last few months, and one gets hardened. Though indeed if it were not for business, I should be glad to be safe again over the seas. It's a fine town, is Dublin. Thou wilt not be from thereaway, I reckon?"

"Nay," said Thorstein; "but I was there a while when Olaf Guthferthson was king, and indeed I was guested in the king's house, and it is now for nought else but to have speech with the queen that I am in York."

"Then, my lad, thou art a bit late; and a good job for thee too, if those rascals—how they shout! —get into the castle."

" She is gone then ? What, is she dead, poor thing ? "

" Nay, not so bad as all that. You see it was something o' this way. Olaf owed a deal to Earl Orm, for without him he would never have halved England with Eadmund. And Orm is a good business man, and looks ahead. Says he to Olaf, If anything happens now to Eadmund, thou wilt be king of all England ; and what shall I get that helped thee thereto ? Says Olaf, What wilt have, friend ? Says Orm, There's my Aldith should be wed ; queen of York is not bad, and Queen of England is better. Says Olaf, Well, says he, King Harald Fairhair had more wives than one. Nay, nay, says the Earl, that's out of fashion nowadays, and I doubt if the Minster-folk would stand it ; the King of York is a good Christian now, my lord, and behaves as such, eh ? So Olaf he goes to the Irish queen and My dear, says he, a sad unhealthy spot is York city ; better go back to Ireland. Says my dame to me—but come in, man, and make thyself at home. Any news from Dublin will be welcome to the mistress."

So he brought Thorstein into the living-room behind the shop. It was crowded up with their goods, and looked like a poor place after the great halls of the Northmen ; but everything was rich and rare. Such hangings to the beds, such carved work in the tables and stools, such shining copper pots and pans ! And the merchant's wife was dressed as grand as a queen, Thorstein thought, with brooches and rings for a dozen. The children even were finely clothed, though they would have looked but blue and wan alongside of the apple-cheeked rogues from the Northmen's homesteads.

"Dame, it's all right; the doors are well barred, and if they break them there is the earth-house to hide in. But see, here's a young man has been in Dublin."

"Welcome, friend," said she, "and what news of the old country?" Thorstein could see with half an eye that the Dane's wife was Irish, and so he replied, saying that it was a good while since he was in Ireland, but he was now come to speak to the queen, who had been friendly with him once. At which Master Dane screwed up half his face and winked, and his wife shook her head at him, and said the queen was a good body, and sorry she was for her, and pity it was they had not gone back together with her to Ireland.

"Nay, nay," said the Dane; "business is business. Keep your shop, say I, and your shop will keep you."

"Well, then," said the wife, "keep thy shop, my lad, and this young man will take a bite, and be the readier to lend a hand if needed."

So she set food before him, and he ate. And while he ate he turned over in his mind the chances about Raineach. Soon he burst out, "Mistress, is it true, as the master says, that all the queen's folk are clean away and out of the castle?"

"Aye," she said, "and a burning shame it was; but better for them maybe. They got a good ship

to sail in, and good pickings. They were stinted
of nothing."

"They would be a deal about the town before
leaving York, and well known to all?"

"Oh, aye, it was always in and out; they coming
to our shop and we at the castle. Not so bad to
do with, they weren't, for king's folk."

"And did you happen to know a great lass, a
bonny one with red hair, a bower-may that the
queen made much of, Raineach by name?"

"And what of her?" asked the dame.

"Oh, she was just one of them in Dublin."

"Was she that? Ah, she was a sad one if ever
there was. Hey, man, hark here! The young
man would have news of that great, strapping,
red-haired wench, her that the castle-folk were
always fighting about."

"The minx!" shouted the merchant from the
shop. "Never heed her, lad, wherever she is."

"All the men were after her," went on the
dame, "and never a one would she take. And
that proud with folk, she might have been a king's
daughter. I'll be bound she was no good, though
the queen was always abetting her. Olaf would
have let them stone her for a witch, one time, but
the queen got her off. She'll be gone with the
rest."

It was little help he would find there, Thorstein
said to himself; but angered as he was, spoke fair;
and said he would take a turn at the look-out while
the master came to his supper. But the tumult
had died down, and the rabble was dwindling as

speedily as it had gathered. The stir was over like a summer storm, and evening had come. Thorstein asked where he could find a lodging for that night, and said he was not penniless. The Dane merchant said he would be glad to board him, but one might see there was little room for guests in house or shop. Nevertheless, there was close at hand a house of priests called St. Peter's, where travellers were lodged, and he would set the stranger on the way when all was quiet.

So Thorstein came to St. Peter's (the place that was afterwards called St. Leonard's Hospital) which Athelstan had founded not long before, giving to the Minster priests a thrave, that is twenty sheaves, from every plough-land in the bishopric, that they might entertain strangers and do good to the poor and sick. There he was received, and no questions asked; and they gave him supper in the great hall, and a place to lie down for the night among other wanderers and wayfarers. Some of them were decent folk, some ugly-looking enough to make Thorstein feel for the few silver pennies he carried, and tuck his poke well into his sleeve, and loosen his weapon in its sheath, before shutting his eyes. But he slept safely, still seeking even in his dreams for Raineach, who was now farther away than ever.

When day was come, and the doors were opened, the priests' officer gave each wayfarer a cake of bread and bade him God speed. Thorstein stood there in the doorway with his dole in his hand, and sore doubt in his heart which way he should turn.

East or West was all one to him. The Minster
bells broke out into a chime, and pealed through
the air. Sweet and sunny it was after last night's
riot and unrest. He bethought him that this was
the Lord's day; he could not leave York without
at least hearing a service, now that he was a
Christian man once more.

People were going all one way in the streets,
but quietly now, and very unlike the crowds of
yestereven. He followed them and went with the
stream into the shadow of the Minster tower and
up the great steps, gaining one at a time in the
throng at the porch. Presently he was carried
through the dark door, and inside as into some
sudden astonishing turn of a dream. For it was
wonderful broad and lofty in there; the walls
betwixt the arches and above the ranks of columns
were inlaid with polished marbles, painted with
long processions of deep-robed saints and emblems
of glory, lit with glimmering, flower-like windows
of glass, and ceiled with canopies of carven work,
with beams and bosses wrought curiously. It was
the building of archbishop Alberht not long since
finished; the new church risen on the ruins of
the old church that Halfdan's Danes had burnt;
witness to the life and might of the faith, a noble
monument of craftsmanship. Its gilding was yet
untarnished and its rich colours were as if fresh
from the hands of the artist; a marvel to behold,
even for a traveller who had been in many lands
and had seen the dwellings of great kings, and
temples both of the old faith and the new.

Thorstein knelt on the paved floor, and beside him and around him knelt the people, men and women, rich and poor ; maybe among them many who last night had been foremost in the tumult, side by side with those they had attacked to rob and slaughter. Far off, in the twilight of the choir, re-echoed from roof and aisles, came the sound of the singing and the solemn voices of the priests ; the very psalms and prayers that were heard in little Cartmel church among the mountains, and in every church of Christian folk from thence throughout the round world. Everywhere the same, and in every age. For to think of the abidingness of it all! Kings came and went, nations rose and fell, but the church drooped its head only to raise it more gloriously. Year by year, while battle and plague were raging without, within the Minster welled, as from a healing spring, the same unending litany for peace from poor folk to the poor folk's God.

No prayer said Thorstein as he knelt thus, while the voices from the choir rolled forth like gathering thunder, or murmured through the aisles uncomprehended like the wind in winter trees. It was enough for him that he was in a holy place, in the palace of God, in the very presence of the King of Heaven. Surely the Lord Christ there, somewhere in the dim bewilderment of gold and gloom, amid those cloudy odours and mysterious answerings of music, surely He was looking forth. And what was the word ? The Lord looketh at the heart. Peace, then.

## CHAPTER XLIV

### WOOD-BIDERS

VERY home-sickness, and nothing else, drew Thorstein back to Furness. He stayed awhile in York, hoping for news; but the only news was of Olaf's death, sudden and strange—the hand of God manifest, folk said, and St. Balthere's vengeance on the church-burner. So all was fear and flight in the old city and throughout Yorkshire.

Then Thorstein took leave of his friend the Dane merchant, and shirking talk with the Minster-priests, won his way back over the Keel, and wandered homewards.

Out of the Northmen's land he was free from their laws. But in those days a stranger was a stranger, in whatever land he abode. If he had no strong friends he was nought. So that between wandering abroad and wood-biding at home there was little to choose.

Now the way of the wood-biders was this. When a man was utterly outlawed no friend might receive him, under pains and penalties; every enemy had the right to hunt him like a wild beast, and to get the reward for killing him, if reward were offered. So there was nothing for it but to stay in the forests, hiding in some cave or secret hut of tree-boughs and turf, and living on what he could hunt, or maybe rob from the neighbours who had put him out of law. In this manner, not so long afterwards, William of Cloudeslea and Robin Hood fled to the greenwood, where the king's sheriffs could not take them. And even to these days, men who have been in trouble with the law have been known to hide themselves in the wide woods that cover the Furness fells, skulking by day and prowling by night; sometimes friendly enough with the poorer sort, and troublesome only to the gentlefolk and greater farmers of the neighbourhood, whose stock they pilfered; and their hiding-places are well known to those that know the country well. In the end these wood-biders either got their peace with the law, or were hunted down, or died like wild beasts in the wood.

Thorstein was not without hope that his business might be done by his friends, whom he never doubted. But when he came one morning to Lowick, risking his neck for the sake of news, he heard that things were no forwarder.

" But," said Halldora, " hark to this. Two days ago, as I was sitting in the sun—it was bright autumn weather—and the child was kicking about on the grass, I heard him crowing and chuckling; and I looked up from my sewing, and there he was, staring at somewhat, and laughing. Then I was ware of one among the trees hard by—for it was on the edge of the wood—looking eagerly at us through the branches. I could see nothing but the gleam of an eye, and a white hand. I made no stay, but caught up the barn and ran for it. And yet by the white hand, I reckon yon was a woman ; and none of the folk hereabouts, be they fell-folk or farm-folk, by the same token. But by the gleam of eyelight, I reckon she was gradely tall for a woman. What dost make of that, lad ? "

He went straight to Greenodd, caring nought who might meet him. Into the hall he strode, and " Mother," said he, " where is Raineach ? "

She was not so very far to seek after that ; nor so very hard to suit when he found her. The true tale had come out on both sides. Unna had told her of Orm, and of Asdis, and of Thorstein's beguiling, and Raineach had given her own story —how she was carried to York, after finding that Thorstein had left thinking of her ; and then of her adventures at Olaf's castle there ; and then how they were sent away, and sailed round by Pictland and Orkney and the South-isles ; and then how the wind had brought them to the Cumberland coast, and how she wept at the sight of her fells again ; and how the queen was sorry for her, and said at last, " There, wench ; hie away with thee, and have better luck than to be a king's castaway." —" And maybe," said Raineach, reddening, " she was a bit weary of me, for there was always some stir forward, and she had no man now to keep her folk under. Any way, by dint of this and that, I made shift to get clear of them all ; and short was the way hither, for fells are easier to pass than foes."

O but Raineach was grown great and strong,

and more than womanly, for she was such a one
as a giant's daughter should be; but as fine spoken
and as fair-skinned as a princess, with her three
winters of court and castle-biding. She had got
used to outlandish doings and unkid havings, one
could see that by the very way she supped her
porridge. But when Thorstein told her to think
twice before she took him—and he did so—how
she laughed! The rose-red came and went, up
and down the bonny slim cheeks. She reached
out both her hands, and held his. It was good to
feel that firm grasp.

"How many times dost thou reckon I have
thought of it, lad, before now?"

They walked together over the fells by woodland paths where none could spy them, to a little
village near the shore of Duddon firth. There
they found the priest whom Raineach had known
of old, he who had given that counsel to her when
she sold her cross to the wood-wrights. He was
a strange figure, with high shaven brow and hair
long behind; the beard thick above his mouth,
and cropped below. And his little church was
more like a hut of the fell-folk than the clay daubing
at Cartmel; for he was one of the old sort, and
of the rule of those Irish priests who came over
sea and settled up and down the Cumberland
coasts, building them stone cells, and there serving
those Irish saints, like Patrick and Sanctan and
Bega, whose names are still known hereabouts,
and were known long before the York Minster-
priests came to that land.

There was no grand wedding, with neighbours to feast and gifts to scatter. They knelt alone in the bare little cell before the priest, and in his own speech he blessed them in the name of the Father and Son and Holy Ghost, and bade them be one heart and soul, world without end. It was no wedding at all, the heathen Northmen would have said, this of the outlaw to the stranger, unwitnessed and unwarranted. But then, to the Christians the bridals of the Northmen were nothing, no more than a manner of partnership in trade, that could be on and off like any other bargain in worldly matters.

It was Thorstein's hope to rebuild his own house at Blawith, if he had to do it with his own hands, none aiding him. And if he could but settle there again and hold his own, far away as it was from the neighbours and buried in the woods, he thought the turn of the tide would come, and after a while he would be once more a free man among his own people. So he knocked up a shed among the ruins, and gathered together such trifles as he could save out of the wreck. But they had not been a week at work on the new home, when before daylight one morning the dogs awakened them, and they fled into the wood, only just in time. Their little cot was ablaze, and a band of armed men was slashing about, and hunting for them up and down.

But they would not leave hope, so fully persuaded as they were that better days were coming. It was the back-end of the summer by now, and winter was upon them. It would not do to risk another door-doom; and as they cowered in hiding—wood-biders well skilled in the craft—they talked out a plan to put more than dry land between themselves and their enemies, until the time should come when they might get peace.

In the midst of Thurston-water there is a little island, lying all alone. When you see it from the fells, it looks like a ship in the midst of the blue ripples; but a ship at anchor, while all the mere moves upbank or downbank, as the wind may be. The little island is ship-like also because its shape is long, and its sides are steep, with no flat and shelving shores; but a high short nab there is to the northward, for a prow, so to speak; and a high sharp ness to the southward, for a poop. And to make the likeness better still, a long narrow calf-rock lies in the water, as if it were the cockboat at the stern; while tall trees stand for masts and sails.

The island is not so far in the water but that one can swim to shore, not so near that it would be easy to attack it without a boat; and at that time boats there were none on these lakes, except maybe a coracle or two of the fell-folk. For fishing, no spot could be better, nor for hunting, if one wanted a safe home and hunting-tower. And if need were to run down Crake to Lowick for news or victuals, that could be done with little risk. This should be their hold and their home, they planned. Here they would make themselves secure, and let the storm drift over their heads.

So said so done. By nightfall they were on the island, with little goods indeed, but with a fire alight, and a rough lair of branches wreathed to shelter them. Into it they crept, and cuddled together as when they were children, laughing at their makeshifts and eager over their designs. Through the shivering, falling leaves the moon shone, patterning the grass of the glade in their dell, and dying out as the clouds raked by ; flashing again, and fading. The woof of the waves against the rock-wall of their castle, and the voice of the wind flying past, booming in the great forest that rose steep over against them on the eastern shore, and then shrieking in the branches overhead—all these touched them not in their shelter, and only made their peace more peaceful, and their security more secure. It was the old time come again for both of them, and they were as lightsome as children in their new happiness.

" Hark to the wind," said Raineach, " afar and away there ; it will be down at the water-foot now, ruffling the great oak trees as if they were barns' curly heads. It is coming upbank. Ah, it is catching the nab end ; hark to the dash of the waves on the shore and on the rock in the water. Here it comes. That was a big one, Thorstein ; it made the ground shake, like a ship-deck. I had liefer be here than on shipboard, though. Shall we hold, thinkst thou ? "

" Oh aye ; the trees sway a bit and the roots jar in the mould ; but we are snug enough here. It's not the wind will harm us."

"Nay, the wind is bonny. It sings. They used to sing a deal in Dublin, the bards, and there were your skalds, they called them, in York; whiles they sang me songs all to myself. They were fools. It was like this: The red fern is tall and fair. She sways in the autumn breeze. Swords flash: blood flows. The red fern heeds them not. Nay, nor I didn't. Not I. They sang nought. But yon wind, what does it sing? Home again, child: home again, old playfellow: home! Make a hole, lad, through the bield to spy at. There's no window in our island palace; and I want to see the fells, and count them. Nay, then; it's no use; we are all umbered up with trees. Aigh! it is wolf dark; pull the boughs again, Thorstein; the wind blows at me through the spy-hole."

"The pet of Dublin and the pride of York has got over nice and nesh with her queens and earls and such like, I doubt, for a bield in the wild wood. Nay, don't nip like that, Raineach; it hurts, thou great rough minx!"

"I'll be named no names then. Did I hurt thee? Truly? Beat me. But thou, Thorstein, never cast up against me what was none of my doing. I did no wrong to thee, of all people. None. The wind knows. Hark, it begins again. What is it saying? The red fern grows round the tall great stone, out on the fell; on the fell. And it grows and it grows, and it hides it, and it smothers it, and it chokes it, all in its red, red hair!"

"Oh let be, lass; I am that weary. What is

the night for but to sleep? It will be up and doing, over soon."

"There, then, shut eyes. Bad lad, they are not shut. I can see them, I can see them in the dark, shining. Dost thou mind the wild cat, Thorstein, and how angry we were? Now we are never to be angry again, are we? Shut eyes and snore, I say, or I'll beat thee."

## CHAPTER XLV

## ON THE ISLAND

HERE as the days went on they made their home.
It was no great job to build a cot in the gap between
the two ridges, the twin backbone of the island;
for the rock on either hand is steep like a solid
house-wall for more than a man's height, and runs
thus maybe two hundred feet, now choked with
ruins of the old building that once stood there;
but formerly a deep and sheltered trough.

They had only to roof it over with poles, which
they cut from the trees growing on the spot, and
to thatch it with boughs and turfs like one of those
huts the woodcutters and bark peelers make themselves even nowadays in the woods. Then they
built up the ends, leaving doors and windows, and
there was as snug a home as might be in all Lakeland. Nor so long a task was it, either, for a lad
like Thorstein, who many a day before had enter-
prised to build a house for the folk of Heathwaite
fell.

And then he bethought him of a bit of a boat,
to make the shoreward journey easy. For himself,
he could swim like a duck; but to ferry another,
and to fetch such things as kind friends might
give, not to say for fishing and fowling, and for
watching the shores of his mere, something more

was needful than swimming-strokes and a wet sark.

The fell-folk had their own old way of boat building, which was this. They cut a tree, and trimmed its ends with the axe ; and then, heating cobbles in the fire, they burned out the heart of the log and hollowed their canoe. But a North-man born, who was no mean woodsmith, thought scorn of that ancient makeshift. And yet to save time, he was content with bent boughs, and withys to bind them into a framework, and skins stretched around all ; making a coracle light to lift and easy to drive, even when the water was none so lound. For our lake-waves never run high like sea-billows, though the strength of the breeze and its sudden gusts sometimes give a rower hard work to keep head to wind. And the many sharp rocks and cobbly shoals upstanding beneath the water-line are somewhat dangerous for a heavy boat under way ; but with a light craft it is light work. And no sweeter life could be dreamt by one to the manner bred than this fishing and fowling on a teeming mere, aboard of a handy little thing that answers every touch and wish of the rower.

So thus they lived as if life were one holiday : safe from prowling beasts and far from mankind. Now and again Thorstein would travel down Crake to his friends, who helped him willingly with goods and tools and porridge-meal for housekeeping. And yet it was little they lacked, to be better off than they used to be in early days among the fell-folk. There was the same hunting ground ; fire-

wood and the sweetest of water in plenty; and
well they knew, if any did, how to make the most
of the wilderness and all it held, and when that
was done to be content.

For a long while nobody meddled with them.
It seemed as though they had been forgotten.
And just to be let alone, and to be together, was
enough to make the morning bright and the
evening merry. Winter was not so sharp, down
there by the water, as it was on the fells. The
lake freezes over but seldom, and even the hard
weather was friendly to them, for it sent beasts
and birds down from the high lands to milder
grounds, and so to their larder; and the warm
feathers and furs were welcome for clothes and
bedding.

When the spring came, and lilies made the
shores all golden, and the snow on the great fells
dwindled into delicate lacework, white in the blue
air, then Raineach was glad of the sunshine to sit
in, at the land-locked harbour, plying her needle,
while Thorstein was away in the boat fishing. He
was never so far but she could climb upon a rock
and spy him out, a speck upon the broad water-
line. Then she would wave to him, and if he was
not busy with a fish he would wave back. So it
was not lonely. After the worry and weariness of
the court, where there was no true friend to count
on, it was the merriest company. The loneliness
was when she was lost in the crowd.

But when the bluebells lay thick upon every rock
ledge of the island, sweet smelling and bluest blue

in their fresh green leaves; when the cuckoos called loud from shore to shore, and the sun was strong, looking down into the depths of the still water and counting every different stone, laid clear and fair in its crystal bed, and the minnows flickered over them; then sometimes she would weep a little to herself as she sat. She could not tell why, if it were not that she was in dread of the time when he would be again among his own people, and hers the less; when she would have to be as any other house-mistress, and his the less; judged by their words and fettered by their ways. Then life would no longer be so free and so loving as it was to the wood-biders.

But when the spring flowers were all gone and the nights were sultry and dark again, she wept no more, for she had new company: a little thing that reached out its hands to her from the bundle of furs where it lay, and that made such quaint faces as were a wonder and a lasting gazing-stock. There was time now for nothing but to watch it, and fondle it, and feed it; and if at first the island was a sweet home to her, now it was more lovely than ever, to be there with her big man, and her little man, and none to let or hinder.

After a while they made a great journey over the fells, and came to Duddon side again, to the strange old priest, that he might christen the child. They called it Swein after Thorstein's father, as in duty bound, though the priest halted somewhat at the name, so outlandish and unchristian as it seemed to his way of thinking. However, he blessed the child, and bade it prosper, and they took their way home without mishap; and the journey gave them talk for many a day to follow.

So they won through the second winter, with never a thought of wearying either of one another or of their home. Now they cleared a little thwaite of land over against the island, and kept a goat or two, and sowed a patch of oats, so that their porridge-stuff need not be so far to seek, and milk for the barn should be plenty. And the summer went by in game and glee, and they had no fears for the winter.

For a Yule-gift they got another guestling, whom they carried in a while to the priest, tripping through the woods with him in his mother's arms, and the sturdy Swein on his father's shoulder. They called the baby Thorstein; and when they saw him and his brother wax and thrive, they laughed a bit sometimes to think of the day when they should take their piglings that Unna had foretold, to show the grandame at Greenodd.

Yet with all this well-being there was somewhat wrong. What with his own labour and his strong friends, Thorstein got all he wanted for bed or board; and with a sweet wife and bonny barns he was set up with the best of company. Over and above which, he knew in his heart that he was now no outcast of holy church, though seldom he saw priest or heard those words of life he had stumbled at long since. Nowadays, what talks he had with Raineach, and reasonings of unknown things, piecing together his scraps of learning with hers, as an old wife plans patchwork; for all the bits must fit into the pattern, whether or no they matched.

And some bits would not fit, such words as told folk to be at one among themselves, and that promised peace between mankind. There was he, out of law and no man's neighbour. Peace with God his heart told him he had; but peace with man was still far to seek; and if all he had done, and all his friends had done, gave him not that peace, how could God command it? How would God provide it?

And being no dreamer, but a man with his eyes open, he knew right well that, if to-day was fair, to-morrow might be foul. So far his foes had given him a wide berth; but says he, "When I am gone, who will take my lads by the hand, and give them their place among their fellows, and assure them land and living?"

"Heed it not," Raineach would answer. "Are not they as well as thou in God's hand?"

"Who heeds it?" he would say. "Not I. And yet!"

"Oh, man, speak fair and be thankful."

"I do speak fair, and I am thankful," said he; "and yet!"

## CHAPTER XLVI

### *UNBIDDEN GUESTS*

But what about Asdis, all this while? She was never the worse off, whatever happened. She was too wise to spoil her looks with weeping, and too pretty to sit long at Asmundarlea waiting for a new husband. She lighted on her feet, like a cat, wherever she fell, and before many months was purring by another fireside, with the cream of the milk to lap. But as she blinked in the fireglow, she was only watching her mouse.

The land was not so bare of people as it had been twenty winters since. Bit by bit, as the days went on, the dales were cleared and inhabited. From the low country one after another went up to take land among the fells. For the Northmen could never abide close quarters. They hated towns, and loved a free life : a spot to themselves, with elbow-room ; a seat on a howe overlooking broad fields and fell-pastures, with the smoke of the next neighbour's hall rising far away through the green wood. It was one thing to have good friends within hail and call, but another to be thrust among folk in one of those stinking swine-styes, said they, where the Saxons herded. And so their biggings crept up from the shore of Leven and Duddon, and from nook to nook the house-reek rose, like bale-fires lighted to tell the world that this Lakeland was the land-take of the Northmen.

Therefore all the coming and going of Thorstein could not fail to be spied, and the tale sped from mouth to mouth, time and again, and lost little in its travels. In a while it came to dame Asdis, where she sat with black anger in her heart against Thorstein, and against the wild she-wolf of the fells who had stolen him out of her arms. And in all this she blamed herself never one whit, and folk came to look on her as a fair woman with great wrongs to avenge.

In a time of quiet, when ill men are aweary of peace, and stirring men hanker after the adventures of old days, no great work was needed to egg on rough fellows to the job she had on hand. A gang of lads and louts was drawn together, and some silly vow got out of them that they would rid the land of the wood-biders; and all as if it had been some great deed.

Now the island was but very little known to the North-folk at the back of the fells; but one thing they knew, and this was that they could not come at it without boats; and if they stayed boat-building they would be spied and foreset. But, said Asdis, "Wait until the apple drops. Why build a boat to cross a bridge?" At which they gaped, but she bade them watch the birds and the bushes.

For that third winter began to be a hard winter. The swallows went early, and the wild swans came in flocks from the north. Choups and holly-berries reddened the hedges; and after Yule the fells were creamed over and the becks dwindled. As the days lengthened so the cold strengthened, until even the sunny shores of Leven and Duddon were frozen fast; and when a high tide came, it burst the floe, and left the sands and mosses strewn for many a mile with huge blocks and tables of ice, piled one upon another like peats to dry. Then Asdis rubbed her hands and said, " Now, lads, your bridge will be built."

So they set out and away through the snowy woods until they came to the waterside of Thurston-mere; and there was a sight. Still as death the white fells stood around. Still as death the lake spread, white and black; white where the snow hid it, and black in great reaches that could hardly be known from standing water, but that its soft ripples stirred not, and the picture of wood and fell lay upon them clearer and quieter than the shapes in a tarn on a summer day, for all the north-wind's blowing. The only thing that moved was a wreath of smoke on the fell-side over against them, and the likeness of the same wreath in the glassy field below. And where the two wreaths met was a crag, standing up from the flat; an island no longer.

They adventured from the snowy shore, hardly knowing when they were on land and when on lake, until suddenly, beneath their feet, deep down, they saw the stones lying at the bottom, clear in the sunlight, through the wonderful floor, such as the floor of Heaven may be to them that walk upon it, and look down upon us thence. Slowly now and warily the men went, for the ice was smooth and slape ; and if it was roughened at all, it was not with waves, but as if stars and arrow-heads of crystal had been inlaid in glass, like the silver a smith inlays in steel.

Then as they walked there arose a strange turmoil in the stillness. Far and wide the ice began to crack and settle, with groanings and thunderings that roared and muttered from shore to shore. Across the black, clear deep there flew white, ragged lightnings, on either hand, before and behind, as when one watches a thunderstorm in the valley beneath a lofty mountain. Then a great crack flitted screaming right under their feet, and half the company turned and scattered, crying out there was witch-work in it, and they were lost. But as they staggered and slid and fell others cursed them for fools, and kicked them up again, and egged them on ; showing them how to set feet together and shove themselves along with their spears thrust hard behind them upon the ice. And so they won a mile or so to the island.

But before they were half way over, the smoke shot up into a thick cloud, and flames flickered ; and over the waste of white and black, above the moaning and groaning of the ice field, arose the deep note of a horn, stifled and quivering at first, and strengthening into a hollow peal, that suddenly stayed. As suddenly it was answered from the fell, and then again from the Beacon hill behind, and then again far down the valley, and then again far up the lake, until the sky was ringing with it. They stood in amaze to listen; and the flame blazed higher, and the smoke rolled in coils, brown against the white moorland. Again the war-horn pealed, and the answers came; and when the last had died away, another answer, over and above the echoes, a faint clang, far down the Crake. And then there was only the groaning of the ice to hear; and the island, when they came to it, was nothing but a snowy rock, untenanted, for aught they could see, and lifeless, but for the great fire.

All round the brink the slape ice shelved away, by the settling of the lake, so that footing was bad to get. The rock went down sheer into the smooth floor, grey and bare beneath and heaped with pillowy snow above, from which hung fringes of icicles, like teeth of a dragon in northern deeps. They scrambled up the shelving slide, and grasped at the rocks to break away the icicles and beat down the snow, for hand-hold and foot-hold. But as they strove up the lower rocks, half smothered with the mealy drift, two heads came out upon the top of the crag, and two great stones rolled among them. And those they fell upon cried but once.

Then began a storm of stones from above, to which they could make no reply, for the defenders were hidden behind the highest ridge, and safe from shot. Even if the attackers could make a shift to use bow and dart, and that they could do seldom in their eagerness to win upward, and in their unsteady footing, their weapons only rattled down among them again from the icebound rock. And so this went on for a while, until many had been maimed, and some killed outright. The nearer they got, the steeper and more dangerous were the battlements of that castle built without hands : a long wall, high enough and steep enough to be difficult any day, but hopeless in this snow and frost, with the great stones plunging down, well aimed from above.

They drew off to the open and held council. In a while they broke into two bands, and went round the island to try for scaling spots, and to break in on both hands at once. Now the ends of the island are less brant than its sides, for there is a way up between the ridges, both to north and south. But nobody who meant to hold the place would fail to stop those doors with some stockading at least, if not a good stone wall ; and so they were brought to a standstill here as heretofore. The north end was not only well blocked, but the rocks there are stiff and steep for this work ; and of the two defenders one followed each company round about, never leaving them alone, what with stones, what with hand-strokes when they tried the wooden palings. And if fire was hot within the hold, it was all frost without, and never a spark to set the doors alight.

So now they met together at the south end, where the twin harbour lies between the calf and the crag. They began to swarm up a buttress that makes a narrow ladder to the top, easy enough to climb if it were not for the ice that sheeted it, and for the rough welcome that awaited the first man on the sharp and perilous crest. By this the far-away fells stood rosy red and dim around; the sky was like fire behind Beacon fell, and the cold floor of ice seemed to be all one lake of blood. The bale on the crag reeked and roared, and out of the smoke came a sword that lopped the first comer like a bough, and sent him rolling down the un-broken rock for many an ell. Then they were aware of the wood-biders standing over them, each with a weapon. They took heart and shuffled up the harder, shouting curses, and what they would do when they won to the top. But the next comer rolled into the bay with his brains knocked out. That was the doing of a big stick that swung round and about in the hands of Raineach.

"Well done, lass," shouted Thorstein, who kept his distance from her, however. "It's not for nothing she's a giant's daughter," he laughed, for he was warming to the work.

But then the children waked behind them, stirred by the noise; and they screamed. Raineach was scared lest some of the rascals had got in the back way, and she flew to seek them. The carles below set up a jeer, and three or four flung in at once. One was down, and another was down; but Thorstein's sword bent; and as he kneeled on it to straighten it, the others were at him. They had him on his back, and a stroke would have done their job; but out came Raineach with such a winging batt of her club on the one of them, as broke his backbone like a rotten stick; and she gripped the other by the throat and hauled him off. She lugged and tugged, and fairly lifted him off his feet, and bundled him over the edge among his fellows. Up springs Thorstein with a great shout, and she beside him; and every mother's son that could stir a limb scattered off the edge in a flock. The weight of them all coming down together broke the ice where it was rotten from the warmth of the flat rock, that caught and kept the morning sun; and they went into the hole like corn into the miller's hopper. It was deep there; the rock goes down at once into the lake, and rises again in ugly teeth, bound to cut a swimmer's knees, let alone the edges of the broken ice. He with the lopped arm, their leader in the assault, after a few wild strokes went down in a red spot. The rest struggled out, to the nearest shore, and shouted themselves hoarse with their anger.

Thorstein and Raineach went up to look at the man whose back was broken. He cried for water, and she gave him to drink. Thorstein stood over him, fierce and stern.

"Who sent thee, man?" he said.

But they got nothing out of him, and in a while he died.

And then, when all was over, Raineach burst into a blurt of weeping. "What, lass! What, lass!" said Thorstein, as she shook and sobbed in his arms; "hold up, my little one; all's right now. I warrant we see no more of them. There's not a scratch on thee, and I am none the worse

but for a bruise or two. What's there to greet
for ? "

" It's not that," she sobbed.

" Here, then ; take the barn. Hark how he is
crying on his mother." Then as the sobs shook
her, and the baby at her breast, said Thorstein,
staring at them, and biting a twig, " Eh, queer
things women are. Aye, and," says he, " there's
women and women."

And so Asdis goes out of the story.

When the stars were shining, they had
more guests, not unbidden, though late to the
play.

" Kinsman," said Hundi, as he panted and caught
his breath, between draughts of milk in the cot on
the island ; " kinsman, no more of this. To the
Althing thou goest this midsummer, if I drag thee
yonder by the scruff of the neck." And, " Aye
goes he," said the half score of men that had come
hot-foot from Lowick.

" Never saw I woman more scared than Halldora
when thy horn sounded."

" Scared was she," said one of them ; " but for
a scare, oh boys, the master capped all. Snail ?
says I, as I peltered after him. Hare ! says I—
Hundi Harefoot's the word ! "

Hundi caught him by the hand, laughing. " A
forfeit," he cried, " to fasten the name ! But
Thorstein, my man, get thy peace, and let us share
it. Life is not worth living, with this horn-
blowing to look for."

So when midsummer was come, Thorstein set

forth alone, sorely as Raineach grudged his leaving her. She said it was for no good he was going. But he kissed her, and said she should be mistress of Blawith before the summer was out. "That may be," she said, "but never so happy as here."

## CHAPTER XLVII

## THE HOST OF WEIRD

THORSTEIN travelled over the fells to the waterhead of the great lake we call Windermere, meaning to stay there for the night, and so to come upon the Althing when folk were at their meeting about mid-day. But when he was at the· door of the Welshmen's cots, in that old ruin of the Romans, there was a great noise within; and he spied a many Northmen sitting there at drink, and among them some faces he knew and misliked. They, too, were on their way to the meeting; and no sooner did he darken the door but they leapt up and ran at him. He had no mind to redden his hands with them, just when he was going to sue for his peace; and away he went, out of the great road and into the woods again.

This was a part he knew but little, and yet he found a track that led him up a steep dell and over a hause where was a wonderful big stone, like a kirk, by the wayside, with high fells running up on either hand. Before him lay the great deep valley, reaching away northward, and all its forests and crags purple and golden in the summer afternoon. Here and there was a gleam of water; and far in the distance, smoke rising as if from the houses of men. The path led onward and downward, rough and steep. He followed it for a good while, and came to a tarn which afterwards they called Brotherwater. Then he was on the floor of the valley, with the steep heights all around and above; and it was but an hour or so to the village of Patrickdale.

This was another of those few spots in the fell country where people were found before the Northmen came into Lakeland. The dwellers were mostly like the rougher sort of Welsh, and their cots were of the poorest, scattered, and buried in wood. And yet they had a chapel in their midst, if it were no more than a cell; where a kind of hermit priest lived, and in the one little chamber slept upon the ground, and ate his crust, and performed the holy service, with nothing but a rough stone for his altar and another for his pillow.

Thorstein sat down weary and hungered at the door, and knocked upon it. Presently there was a barking of dogs that echoed from crag to crag around; and then the door opened, and the priest came out with a thumping big stick upheld in one hand, while he unbarred the iron-hasped door with the other.

Thorstein bade him have peace, for it was a Christian and a wayfarer who begged for alms. So the priest let him into the chapel and from an ark brought out a bowl of sour milk and a cake of rye bread.

" Maybe now," said Thorstein, " this is all thou hast."

" All I have here," said the priest. " But there are good neighbours."

So Thorstein drank the milk at a draught, and ate the cake in two mouthfuls.

" I am no stranger in these parts," said he, " but I never was here before."

They talked together awhile, for the priest seemed right glad of a friendly face other than those of his rough flock—goats he called them, " for lambs they be not indeed, but very mountain goats. And yet God forgive me for saying an ill word of them," added he ; " for I mind me of the days when I was in the world. There was as much hardness of heart and stiffneckedness among our folk yonder at Dacre——"

But now there was a noise without, and the dogs barking again. More than that, eager voices. Out stepped the priest to hear what the news might be, bidding Thorstein stay where he was, or he would not answer for him.

There was a couple of men—fighting-men of Domhnall's they seemed by their weapons ; but no great champions, by their faces. Around them a knot of rough villagers, half clothed in skins, and shaggy-headed, with staves in their hands. They all talked long and loud. Thorstein could just hear something about an army and flight and slaughter ; but he deemed it wise to do as the priest bade him, lest he should be mis-kenned and mauled by that rabble.

" Lord help us," said the priest coming back into the church ; " God and all blessed Saints protect us. Ill tidings, young man. Awful tidings. But as the mountains stand round about Jerusalem, even so the Lord stands round us who fear him."

Then between prayers and sighs he told the news. These were two men of the dale who had gone to fight in Domhnall's army, called out but lately. It seemed that Eadmund the English king had been warring against Domhnall's people and against the Northmen; and having wasted far and wide, he was entered into Cumberland where Domhnall, though he had fled from place to place, thought to make a stand; and so had called out every man he could levy. But still he got the worst of it, and fled before the Saxons; and no wonder, for with the Saxons there were Malcolm king of Scots and a host of his, and Llewelyn of Wales with his men, a terrible great multitude. Last night they lay at Penrith, and Domhnall was pressing his men forward towards the fell-country, hoping either to escape into the mountain fastnesses, or to entangle his enemies in some strait pass among rocks and swamps, and so destroy them. But, before these men fled from his army, it had been given out that he aimed for the deep dale at the back of Helvellyn.

"What," cried Thorstein, "beside our Northmen's trysting place? Aye, father, though I am Christian, I am a Northman born, and neither Dane nor Saxon. Tell me, oh man, tell me how I may come to them and give them warning. Is there a way over yon crags? It cannot be far; and yet the rocks stand up like walls of heaven."

The priest took him to the door and pointed out a deep dale that runs up into the fells : Grizedale we call it now. When he was at the head of that dale he would find a tarn ; then he was to take the valley to his right hand, and it would bring him to the hause above Thirlmere. "But," said he, " it is trackless forest ; none rougher in our mountains. And it teems with wild beasts. If it were for a boar-hunt with a party of stout fellows, no place could be fitter. But for a lone traveller, at speed, and a stranger, I doubt the end of the journey might be nearer than its goal."

" Path or no path, boars or bears," cried Thorstein, running back into the church for his weapons, " I must try it and that hastily."

" Stay," said the priest. " There is another way, if thou canst climb the rocks like a wild cat, and keep a cool head while the eagles scream around thee. I know this only by report ; but men have climbed above the woods where all is open grass or naked rock, and so across over Helvellyn. They say it is a fearful place ; no otherwise than when one mounts a ladder against a castle-wall ; but that this is terrible in its loftiness beyond any high tower or deep sea-crag. And the night is at hand."

" The night," said Thorstein, " is fair, and never wholly dark at this season. As for crags and the dangers of the fells, I have fared through a many before now. Point me out the way, father."

It was the clear gloaming of summer midnight

when he had forced his way through the woods
that clothed the valley side and crept up the crags
like moss on a stone. He was on Striding-edge;
forest and fell beneath him were black, a tossing
surge of darkness; in which gleamed ugly and
strange the great lake, that reached away into distance of slaty gloom. On the ridge there was light
from the north, a brown light, no more than enough
to see footing and hand-hold. But when his foot
slipped, and a great stone rolled from under it,
there was a crash and a roar that raised the echoes
all round the cove, as the stone whirled and leapt
towards the round tarn that he could hardly discern
in the blackness—how far below he could not
reckon. And on the other hand it was no less
steep. Pinnacles of rock stood up along the abyss,
and in front a great mass, a wall it seemed in the
uncertain gloom, unapproachable. With the falling
stones the eagles were roused, and sailed screaming
about him; so that he clung to the ridge, and drew
his sword.

Then he came to a place where the rock fell away
into darkness; and he sat doubting the priest's
guidance, and scanning the black wall that rose
overhead before him, for he was weary by now
and began to be faint with hunger. He cast overboard his shield that he had carried so far, and it
fell down the rock but a little way, and then caught.
He followed it and found it, and then scrambled
up the wall, which turned out to be no more than
a scree-slope, though it was one of the stiffest.

From Helvellyn top he saw the arch of light in

the north again, sunset and dawn in one, streaked with black bars of cloud. But underneath them, strong against the meshes of faint daffodil colour, and the lowest band of dusky red, stood out the lines of Skiddaw and Blencathra, the shapes he knew right well of old, and welcomed joyfully. He ran along the brown and rounded grassy summit, forgetting his weariness, until Thirlmere gleamed beneath him—the winding lake with its steep shores, and the crags where he had first met Aluinn and Domhnall. Then, how high that mountain eyrie of theirs had seemed; but now it was nought but a heave in the dark land that was spread out before him like an embroidered garment cast upon the floor.

Then, as he went forward, wary of the swamps that lie among the grass of those great mountain-backs, he saw a man come up on the moorland, but from some point further north; and run, as he had run, across toward Thirlmere. " He will be another of the fleers," said Thorstein to himself. " He is bound for the Northmen's camp like me." And he shouted, and tried to overtake him, but in vain. Then came up two or three others; they were dimly seen and grey in that twilight, but he could make them out enough to know that they carried weapons, and fled in haste. He shouted again, but no answer. Then more followed, and he could see that among the newcomers were pur-suers as well as pursued; and now one fell, and was killed outright before his eyes. But there was no sound of shouting, and as he ran toward them he seemed to come no nearer, whether it was that the twilight put him out of his reckoning, or what. And then came a flock of men marching forward with banner and spear, aye, and horses among them, and chariots, on the bare mountain-top, with pathless crags behind and in front, where no army could have marched in order, nor waggon have gone upon wheels. But still they crossed over, a very great multitude, under the broken light that held his eyes fixed to northward. He stayed running, and listened. The waterfalls roared beneath, but not a sound was there of living men, neither tramp nor shout, and still they passed.

Terror was upon him now, and his knees shook. He looked behind him, and out of the deep blackness a few great stars shone, and around was the moorland with its strange forms, and he knew not what else, crowding upon him. With a cry he fled down the grassy slope. It fell away steeper and steeper. He stumbled among the hidden stones; but he could not stay his feet, and down he rolled from rock to rock, into the thunder of Helvellyn gill.

## CHAPTER XLVIII

## THE STORM OF
## LEGBURTHWAITE

At Legburthwaite the morning was wild.    The
wind had risen in the night and brought rain.    The
clouds were low, raking along the fell sides, and
one could hardly see the crags across the valley
for greyness.

The Althing was not yet hallowed, for the Northmen were not met together.    Some early comers
had arrived and spent the night in their booths—
rough hut-walls, unroofed, put up of old to serve
for lodging at these summer meetings, and covered,
when the time was, with tent-cloths cast over them.
A group of elder men sat talking in the rain;
others were setting up the bounds of the doom-
ring, driving in the posts with pick and mallet,
and cutting hazel poles in the copse hard by, to
lay across from stake to stake.    Others were
repairing the winter's damage to the turf seats
within the ring, where the chiefs and the jurymen
were to sit.

Down from Helvellyn side, through the driving
rain, crept a battered man, slowly working his way
among the boulders of the slope.    He dragged
himself up to the group of elders, and they saw that

he was newly wounded, and foredone with toil and travel.

Then said one, " This is Thorstein Sweinson of the Mere : he that slew his brother. Away, fellow ; the place is not hallowed yet ; there is no peace to be got now for such as thee."

Said another, " Let be ; the wood-bider is not here for nought, and maybe has a story to tell."

But he gaped upon them and could not speak. So they gave him to drink.

" Thanks, friend," he said. " Neighbours, do with me as you will, but hear me. Domhnall is fleeing before the Saxons. He is upon us even now. Last night I saw two of his men : they had fled to their home in the fells. They said that Eadmund the English king was at Domhnall's heels, and with him Malcolm the Scot and Llewelyn of Wales with a great multitude. Domhnall was for leading them hither, to entrap them if he could ; or to escape into the mountains. I have fled night-long over yon high fells to bring the news. And I have seen them. On the top of the mountains I saw the hosts pursuing and pursued. Whether it was a vision I cannot tell ; but the tidings are truth."

" Here be fine dreams," said the first speaker, " and midsummer madness."

" Dreams or no dreams, the man is spent with travel and battered, and he gives his head into our hands for the sake of the tidings. We shall soon see whether they be true. Meanwhile, my lad, come into my booth and be fed."

Thorstein had hardly brought hand to mouth, when there was a stir without, and the foremost flyers of Domhnall's army came by. They were the guard of the king's wife and children, and a troop of pack-horses with them, heavily laden, maybe with treasure. They made no stay, but for a hasty word, and away toward the burg at Wythburn.

The Northmen, taking short counsel together, agreed to draw out of their booths, and to make a stand upon the rock, the northern spur of Great Howe that stands over against the Castle Crag, and so abide what might happen. Why they should thus meddle, when they might have escaped with the foremost flyers, or easily hidden in the woods, who can say ?—except that they were bred fighting-men, and thought scorn to leave their own Thing-stead without so much as a stroke.

So there in battle array they stood, on their mound where the four dales met, and the great crags around. Over against them the path crept by the skirts of the fells ; on this side the river and on that Helvellyn beck ; and the clouds flying low, and the rain driving.

Out of the mist came the flyers, horse galloping and foot running ; whoever was sound and un-wounded outpacing his fellows, as they streamed up the road and into the mist again. Then came the wearied men, some of them wounded and some scant of breath and half blind with toil and with watching under arms, pushing and pressing along the narrow path ; here and there one falling with a groan, and kicked out of the way into the river, or screaming as the horses stamped the life out of him. And so they swept past, while the Northmen cried to them across the dale to turn and stand by their friends.

Then there was a pause, and the sound of the pursuers shouting along the vale of St. John; and presently their van-guard was seen pressing along the road—Welsh they were of Llewelyn's company, to whom the foremost place had been given in this enterprise because they were mountain men, and led where the Lowlanders, with all the fire of the chase, sometimes held back from following.

When they came to the place where they could see the Northmen in array on the howe, they were brought to a standstill; and fresh comers behind them crowded at their rear, like the wreckage of a streaming flood, when one great bough is held fast at a force-head. Then they crossed the flat field, and stood on the bank of Helvellyn beck, and cried to the Northmen to come down and yield themselves. But the Northmen shouted in answer, and gave them a flight of spears; and when spears were spent, stones and sods, and everything that was handy. Soon the Welshmen, seeing how few they had to deal with, and how many of their own men had come up by this time, took heart, and rushed up the bank shoulder to shoulder. But along the top it was shield to shield, and a line of whirling blades; and down the wave rolled again.

By this time the main army was coming up, and

the cry was for bowmen. For in those days it was not as it was in later times, when the English foot-soldier carried his long-bow. Spear to throw and axe to hew with, were their best weapons. The Welsh stood aside, and a file of archers passed through the host, and formed in a line on the Thing-field, while the rest ransacked the booths. Together the bowmen drew their bows, and at a shout of command to let fly, the Northmen fell flat under their shields, and the flight of arrows hurtled over them.

But while this was going forward, behind the line of archers other companies crept this way and that; and through the cover of the wood on Great Howe other bowmen climbed up to take advantage of the higher ground, and to get the Northmen below them. And soon there was a rattling on shield and helm and coat of mail. When the enemy saw that they were beginning to be discomfited, spears were levelled, and up they rushed in a thick throng on all sides at once, man pressing man from behind, so that there was no turning nor fleeing. Down went the first comers all round the line of red blades; but the shield that Thorstein had carried, and lost, and saved again, was burst through, and a broken shaft left in it, and the strap was riven. He took it in both hands and hurled it edgewise, and shouted when it caught a big fellow in the teeth and drove him backwards into the thick of the crowd below.

"Well thrown, wood-bider," said his next neighbour. "I'll be thy shield-man this holm-gang;" as he caught a stroke on his target, and Thorstein leapt out from behind him and cut down the man who had given it. So it was hand to hand and sword to spear for a while, over the ring of fallen bodies. But the Northmen shook them off, and thrust them down the brink again.

Then one upon the Thing-stead began to sing, and then another, in staves of verse that seemed to set their fellows' hearts on fire. They shouted at their foes, giving them every ill name and stinging jest that might prick them to a new attack. But the only answer was the hail of arrows from above, and if the rain washed the Northmen white, there was red enough running to need it. Hardly one among them but had some hurt. Thorstein, who was no whole man to start with, and ill clad for this play, was the worse for more than a scratch.

"Neighbours," said he, "why are we standing still to be shot down like deer?"

Then forth he leapt, and down the slope, hewing right and left, and leaving a lane through the crowd. His friends followed close in a band, and the enemy drew back before them, and closed behind them. The Northmen were like a wild beast in a net.

"Look you there," said Thorstein, holding out a bladeless hilt; "was ever such rotten iron?"

"It has done a day's work," said his friend with the shield.

"Nay, not a forenoon's."

He sat down upon a stone. His friend took

him under the shoulder to lift him on. "We shall win through yet," said he.

But Thorstein fell over on the red grass.

"Let be," said the elder who had known him at the first. "He has got his peace. Forward all!"

# CHAPTER XLIX

## DUNMAIL RAISE

KING EADMUND stood upon the brink of Thirlmere, and scanned the shore on either side. His enemies had vanished as if by art magic. There lay the path running down to the ford, and up again on the farther side, and it could be traced winding under the terrible crags whose tops were lost in clouds, and away into huge headlands and shaggy promontories plunging into the water, one beyond another, until they faded afar in the rain and mist.

On this hand King Malcolm, and on that hand King Llewelyn, were instant to go forward and follow the road; but the Lowland king, brave as he was in fight and bold in counsel, hung back from the attempt and from following unseen foes into unknown fastnesses.

While they talked, across the wath came two or three men, gaunt and red-bearded and clothed in skins. They waved their hands above their heads as if to signify that they came in peace; and the king bade bring them before him. At their first words, " King," said Malcolm, " these are folk of mine, or should be; for it is our tongue they have. Let me be interpreter."

Then the fell-folk told the kings that Domhnall and his men were lurking in the woods, ready to roll rocks upon their enemies. But they could show the Saxons how to get the better of the ambush.

Asked by what device, they said that fell-climbers could reach the top of the brow under which Domhnall lay ; and once there, a few men could roll rocks on him as he had meant to roll rocks upon the Saxons ; and then the main army could pursue them along the road, which was no worse than that by which they had come.

" And a good counsel it is, king," said Malcolm, when he had interpreted, " and one that we use often in our mountain warfare. Give the business into my hand, and you shall see them swarm out of the woods like ants out of a stirred anthill."

" But what faith can we put in the word of these savages ? " asked Eadmund.

They said proudly that it was so as they had spoken, and they were in the hand of the kings to reward or to slay. " And beside that," said one of them with a scowl, " we have an old grudge of our own to settle with Domhnall."

So the army moved over the wath, and the main body halted on the road, ready for the chase when the game was beaten out of cover. Malcolm with a band of mountain men, guided by the red folk, climbed the brow of Armboth fell ; and when they were at the top, set to work heaving rocks over the edge. There was a crashing among trees, and shouts and shrieks, and presently men were beheld fleeing down the screes among the woods, and the great stones whirling down after them. Such as got away, streamed out into the road, and fled along it up and down, like worms out of a dunghill when it is beaten to get baits. Then the trumpets were blown that should signal to the men above to leave their work; and forth marched the army in hot pursuit, along the path and along the low foreshore of the lake, and then mounting over the crags where they were high, and descending again among rocks, and cliffs, and wild wood, that overhung the length of the lake. And at last they looked down upon the burg at Wythburn.

Here for a while they were brought to a stand; the walls of great stones, and the swampy flats on one side of it, threatened to hold them longer than they liked. The day was wearing, and if the nut were cracked the kernel was not eaten yet. So they took up their stand on the high ground between the city and the fell, and the trumpets sounded an assault.

Then was there shouting, and a terrible cry that rose to Helvellyn top, as the Saxons clambered up the rugged wall in throngs, and leapt over, bearing down the defenders and slaughtering all before them. Domhnall's wife and his two children were taken; but for the rest it was kill and slay, as men ransacked the rude cots within the walls for their enemies, and hewed them down where they found them.

But while all this was going forward, a band of men was spied making away along the fell side. They had escaped by the farther gate and along the road; and the freshest of the Saxons who were still outside the walls, and the fleetest of their horsemen, were sent in pursuit. But the road was rugged and difficult as ever, and if they came up with one party, and brought it to bay, it was but to waste time, and the rest had the better start of them. And so the battle went on, at every beck to be forded, and every rock to be passed; and especially where the great tongue of land at the foot of Steel fell stands across the valley, like a twin wall of huge earth-works cast up by giants long ago.

The foremost of the flyers was Domhnall himself, running for dear life up the long slope of the pass. He was alone now, and on foot. One horse after another had fallen under him, and of all the army he had led out to its ruin not one was there to stand by him. This man had come between him and the spear that threatened him; that one had turned back to keep the hunters in play. They were gone now; but he was still a king, if the crown on his helmet could make him one. And he bethought him of hiding among the moors and rocks, anywhere, like a wild beast; and he peered this way and that through the rain as he ran, with none following, escaped, he hoped, at last. He neared the brow of the hill; soon it would be down-bank and away; surely some woodland dweller would harbour him.

Under a hawthorn tree at the summit sat a woman, with long golden hair lank in the rain, and green gown wet, and clinging to her sides; hard featured, and fierce she looked; strange, as she rose and stood before him in the way. He dashed at her blindly with his sword, but she caught his hand, and as he stumbled at her feet, the crown fell from his helmet, clattering on the stones of the path. She took it up, and weighed it in her hand.

"Domhnall," she said, "it is mine at last, then?"

"Oh, Aluinn," he cried, "save me, hide me!"

She led him by a roaring stream and up a steep, narrow gill, away from the valley and the shouts of the pursuers, aloft into the cloud. They came to a black water, shoreless, beyond, for the rain-mist. As he sank down, out-wearied, she flung the golden thing into the dark tarn.

"It is safe there," she said.

And there they say the crown of Cumbria lies to this hour, in the depths of Grizedale tarn.

Domhnall passed away into the cloud and was seen no more in these parts. Folk might well believe him to be dead, or gone to fairyland. Whether his flight was spied by some of the Northmen coming over Dunmail raise toward the Althing which they never held, or howsoever it might have been told, the place kept his name, changed but a little in alien mouths; and still haunted, they say, by the fleeing king and the fairy maid flitting before him.

## CHAPTER L

## THE PEACE OF THORSTEIN

TERRIBLE was the tale they brought to Hougun about the battle beneath Helvellyn and the death of Thorstein and his fellows. Though indeed not all of them perished. Hopeless as it seemed, some of that band had cut their way through the Saxon army and escaped into hiding among the rocks and woods, and some that had been left for dead had been found by their friends when the storm was over, and taken up and healed of their wounds. But not Thorstein. He lay where he fell, within a step of the spot where he had slain his brother. They gave him his peace, late as it was; for it was not too late to let his children inherit the land he had taken around Thurston water.

Hundi and Raud, Mani and the rest of their kinsmen and neighbours came together and rebuilt the homestead at Blawith, freely giving their labour as the custom was; and over and above their labour, each comer gave a share toward the things that were needed to keep house and farm. So that with what she had and what she got, Raineach lacked neither servants nor stock, furniture within nor gear without.

They brought her from the island, and bade her dwell in peace on the land that was hers and her children's. Many a time came to her one and another who would gladly have cast in his lot with them for her sake; but she said nay to all. And before Yule she was the mother of a third son to Thorstein, whom she called Gartnaidh after her father, for he was red-haired and long limbed.

"Thorstein of the Mere will not want for sons to avenge him," said folk, when they came to see her.

"Nay," she said. "He has found his peace. Let us keep it."

But a twelvemonth had not gone by after the battle, and midsummer was not yet come, when they heard tidings of the death of Eadmund in his own hall at a feast, by the hands of an outlaw. The North-folk looked at one another, as much as to say it was but his due; vengeance had come upon him already for the strife he had stirred up, and especially for the sackless and innocent men who had fallen with Thorstein Sweinson in the war upon Cumberland.

But the Northmen continued in their homes by firth and fell, spite of York earls and Scottish kings. For yet a hundred years and more they kept their freedom. Their own laws they made at their Althing, now in one spot, now in another. Even when the Normans had brought all this border country under the feudal yoke, still for many a hundred years the dalesmen used to meet at the Steading-stone by Thirlmere, and kept alive some smouldering memory of their birthright in the country Laws of Wythburn. And everywhere they still had their old manners and their old speech, changing little of either, and that but slowly.

The Blawith house endured. Its children lived long in the land. When they increased so that Blawith was too small for them, across the Crake they built a new place, and there they dwelt for many a generation, and thereabouts they dwell even to this day. For in these dales the dream of Unna came true, that saw love abiding and labour continuing, heedless of glory and fearless of death.

So ends the Story of Thorstein